Blairsville Joint
Junior High School

92-Burger
Mas   *798*

	Date Due		
SEP 25	SEP 28		
OCT 15	OCT 30		
OCT 28	SEP 28		
NOV 16	NOV 18 82		
	APR 24		
DEC 3			
JAN 14			
FEB 11			
FEB 5			
MAR 4			
MAY 20			
DEC 8			
MAY 18			
MAR 7 14			
MAY 3			
JAN 20			
DEC 23			
Qui 26			
SEP 28	PRINTED IN U. S. A.		

BAT MASTERSON

(William Barclay Masterson)

Born: November 24, 1853—Iroquois County, Illinois

Died: October 25, 1921—New York, New York

In the brawling, bloody history of the West, few men lived as dangerously as Bat Masterson. Buffalo hunter, Army scout, Indian fighter, sheriff, U. S. Marshal, his reputation as a fast-draw kept law and order in Dodge City and Tombstone—the two toughest towns on the frontier. As a young boy, Kansas born Billy Masterson was given an 1863 Springfield rifle. When, at eighteen, he left the farm on which he lived, his gun went with him as a promise of the adventurous life he would now live. And Billy, later known as Bat, did enjoy an adventurous life as Deputy and Marshal, in his association with Wyatt Earp and in his later years as a prominent New York journalist.

Books by DALE WHITE

GIFFORD PINCHOT
The Man Who Saved the Forests

JOHN WESLEY POWELL
Geologist-Explorer

FAST-DRAW TILGHMAN

BAT MASTERSON

BAT
MASTERSON

by
DALE WHITE

Julian Messner, Inc.   New York

Published by Julian Messner, Inc.
8 West 40 Street, New York 18

Published simultaneously in Canada
by The Copp Clark Publishing Co. Limited

Fourth Printing, 1962

Printed in the United States of America
Library of Congress Catalog Card No. 60-12451

CONTENTS

1. BILLY MASTERSON

WHEN BILLY MASTERSON SPIED A WAGON AND TEAM APPROACH-ing, he forgot about filling the wood box. He dropped his armload of kindling and called his brothers, chopping and stacking wood alongside the sod shanty. "Ed! Jim! Hey, Tommy! Here comes Pa. Race you to the wagon."

Billy sprinted barefooted along the ruts that strung the farm to the far-flung Kansas prairie. Reaching the wagon first, he shouted, "Pa, did you bring any surprises from town?"

Mr. Masterson whoaed the team. He leaned over and rumpled Billy's black, curly hair. "Mebbe."

Billy scrambled onto the large spring wagon. Then he gave a hand to his brothers: fair-haired, handsome Ed, who was fourteen to Billy's thirteen; snub-nosed eleven-year-old Jim and eight-year-old Tommy. "Pa's brought surprises!"

"Honest?" Tommy asked.

"Yup. For them as did their chores, you understand."

Ed spoke up quickly. "I chopped all the stovewood."

"Tommy and I done all we was s'posed to," Jim added.

Mr. Masterson glanced expectantly at his second son. "You, Billy?"

"Aw, I went hunting. But I got ten squirrels and three rabbits. Ma's got rabbit pie in the oven." He squirmed under his father's steady gaze. "It took all day! I didn't have time left over for chores."

"We didn't care," Ed said stoutly. "We'd rather do Billy's chores and have meat for supper."

Mr. Masterson scratched his bearded cheeks, trying to suppress a grin. Billy was a problem. Show him an ax or a milk pail, and five seconds later he had skedaddled for the thickets along the Little Arkansas River. He was harder to pin down than quicksilver; but someone had to be hunter for the family, and Billy had proved himself a born shot. "Well, as long as you provided meat, I guess you did your share," he judged.

Billy grinned. "Thanks, Pa. Hey, when do we get our surprises?"

"After you unload the wagon."

As soon as it stopped in front of the shanty, the boys carried the boxes inside. Billy poked in each one until he found the new pocketknives and horehound candy.

In lifting a sack of grain from the wagon, Ed and Billy uncovered an old rifle. Billy pounced on it. "Pa, where did you get this?"

"Leave it be and finish your work," his father ordered.

"Did you buy it?" Billy examined it eagerly. "It's a Springfield!" He spat on the iron lock plate and polished it with his shirt tail. "Model 1863. What's the eagle on the plate mean?"

"Billy, I told you—" his father began, then gave up. Guns and Billy were like feathers and glue, practically inseparable. "The eagle means it's a government-issue rifle. That's the model folks say won the war for the North. I got it in a swap. Reckon it's seen too much war use to be much good."

Billy peered into the barrel. "It sure is." Just the same, he wanted it badly. "Can I keep it, Pa? That ol' scattergun of Grandpa's I been usin' five years now is about plumb wore out."

Mr. Masterson was agreeable, but he knew his wife would insist it be given to Ed. She made no bones about Ed's being her "angel."

"Ed's the oldest. Reckon he should have first say."

"Billy's the hunter," Ed spoke right up. "Let him have it. We'll share it."

"All right," their father agreed, "just so your mother knows you want it that way, Ed."

Before daybreak the next morning Ed and Billy were on their way to the river. As they ran across the prairie, Billy chortled, "Won't do Ma no good to bang on the dishpan. We'll be too far off to hear." Both knew they would get a caning for ducking their chores, but that seldom kept them from going hunting together.

They knew that, on the south-central Kansas frontier, survival demanded constant labor and sacrifice for a family of parents, four gangling sons, and two small daughters. Although Ed and Billy had been born in Iroquois, Illinois, Ed in 1852 and Billy on November 24, 1853, both had ropy muscles and calluses aplenty to show for their part in the grueling labor of clearing wilderness to cropland. Now they were helping their father make a fresh start on the homestead he had acquired after the Civil War.

Slowing to a trot, Billy sniffed noisily. He liked the scent of the grass that stretched in every direction. Prairie larks shot skyward ten paces ahead, piping shrilly.

"Gonna be another scorcher of a day," Ed remarked, mopping his forehead.

"Lot cooler on the river bottom."

Weeks of breaking sod on the treeless prairie had sunburned Billy to Indian red. His ears and the tip of his nose peeled constantly. "Boy, I can't wait to shoot a deer. Quit laggin'."

Several miles farther, the two plunged stiff-kneed down a clay bank. They moved single file through the brushy river bottom. Cottonwood leaves hung motionless above them.

"Psst!" Billy poked Ed and pointed. His sharp eyes had spotted a fat wild turkey on a tree limb. He held the gun barrel while Ed inserted a cartridge at the muzzle end, tamped it down with the ramrod, and replaced the rod in its groove under the barrel. Then Ed thumbed back the hammer and placed a percussion cap on the nipple. He raised the Springfield, sighted carefully, and fired. Smoke and a flash of flame squirted out from the lock.

"Eeee-yuh!" Ed rubbed his smarting eyes. His shot went far to the left. The turkey squawked wildly and flapped off through the branches.

After smoke stopped curling from the barrel, Billy reloaded. He and Ed waited motionless until the grove quieted. Mosquitoes darkened their bare scratched arms and legs. Finally Billy moved forward. When he spotted a deer, he braced himself against a tree and fired. The bullet plunked into a tree. The deer bounded away.

"Dawgonnit!" Billy fumed, his temper flaring. "I allowed for them sights bein' way off!" He rubbed his smarting shoulder, bruised by the gun's recoil. "No use wastin' any more ammunition till we get this gun fixed." He sighed. "We might as well go home and take our licking."

Ed led the way back to the prairie. "Hey, I just thought of something. Mr. Kown is a blacksmith. Couldn't he rifle the barrel for us?"

"You're right! Let's go see him Sunday." On Sundays the boys were free to do as they pleased.

The following Sabbath Day the two left for Kown's at sunrise. It was eight miles to this nearest neighbor. Now, at daybreak, they saw prairie chickens running down bugs, and brown-eared rabbits lolloping ahead of them.

"Howdy, boys," Charles Kown called from his rocking chair set in the shade of a neat frame house. The middle-aged Scottish blacksmith turned homesteader had a baked-apple-textured face with wiry chin whiskers.

"Morning, boys," Mrs. Kown greeted them. Her peri-winkle-blue eyes matched her long starched cotton dress. "Dad here spied you a-coming. There'll be berry tarts out of the oven before long."

"Oh, boy!" Ed sat on the ground and leaned his back against the house.

Billy was all business. He laid the rifle in the blacksmith's lap, then sat cross-legged at his feet. "What do you think of this Springfield that Pa got in a swap? It shoots crookeder 'n a pig's tail. Could you fix it?"

Kown sighted the gun. At first glance he thought it hardly worth repairing.

"Me and Ed don't expect you to fix it for nothing. We figger on cutting stovewood for two hours today, and bringing you a haunch of venison every now and then."

Kown knew the Mastersons were often hard fixed for food. "I'll do me best. But it's too hot to fire the forge today. You leave it here. I'll have it in fine shape by next Sunday."

Billy hugged his knees. "Golly, thanks. And, Mr. Kown, with the Springfield actin' right, if I ever did see a buffalo—"

"Nay, laddie. Not in these parts. The buffalo are all gone. And remember what I said before. Ye canna shoot the big fellow without a powerful gun."

On their previous visits the blacksmith had entertained the boys with stories about his youth, when he had hunted with the great pathfinder Jim Bridger.

"Ever since you told us about huntin' buffalo, I been hankering to get me a robe," Billy added. "Hey, would you tell us more stories while me and Ed cut your wood?"

"I'd like to hear more about how you and Billy Dixon almost got run down in a stampede," Ed said.

The boys carried Kown's rocking chair to the wood pile. Mrs. Kown disappeared into the house.

After he lighted his pipe the blacksmith began talking about the buffalo country, the vast prairie farther west. When he described the exciting hunt, and the violent storms and Indian attacks, Billy forgot momentarily about cutting wood.

Wagh! he thought, using Jim Bridger's favorite expression. Out in western Kansas there were still millions of buffalo roaming around. A man could make a heap of money being a hunter. Buffalo hides were all the rage now for industrial belting and upholstery. A hunter didn't have to spend one day after another behind a plowhorse, either. For two cents I'd run away. A good shot like me could do all right. But then he remembered, Only it wouldn't be right to leave until Jim can take over the hunting, and Tommy more chores. But someday, Billy Masterson, you are going West!

Just then Mrs. Kown called, "Chicken on the table!"

It wasn't chicken and cream gravy and biscuits that made him explode in a run. It was the promise he had made himself about his future. "Yahoo!" he shouted, bounding over the grass like a young stallion breaking for freedom.

For the next three years Billy and Ed shared the rifle. Six days a week they worked from dawn to dark alongside their father. They helped build a new house, broke sod on one hundred and sixty acres, plowed straight "furrers," seeded, harvested, and fenced. A few short weeks in mid-winter they attended a one-room school.

Every Sunday they went hunting. It was their only recreation and source of pocket money. Each spring they marketed their furs and hides in Wichita.

Tornadic winds ruined the crop in 1868. The next year the

wheat was flattened by hail. But in 1870, thanks to prolonged good weather, Mr. Masterson said, "A few more
days, boys, and we'll start threshing a bumper crop."

Billy's heart turned over with a big thump. At last! If
things worked out good for Pa, he could go West. He didn't
have any money, nor a gun of his own. No matter. He would
get a job in Wichita in the slack weeks after harvest time,
and earn enough to put him on his way.

The next day the family rode to Wichita for an all-day
Methodist Revival. This consisted of three hours of preaching and gospel singing in the morning, then a midday picnic
for all. After the heat simmered down, everybody would
return to the big tent for the Hallelujah and Witness session,
followed by the two-hour sermon on Salvation.

Ed, Billy, and Jim rode to town with their legs dangling
over the end of the wagon. "Know what?" Ed whispered so
his parents and sisters up front could not hear. "This is the
first time we've ever been in Wichita in the summer. The
cattle-shipping season is goin' full blast. We'll see lots of
longhorns and cowboys."

Billy rolled his eyes. "That ain't all we'll see."

He was wise. He knew what all went on in Wichita in
the summer. The tanner where he sold his pelts had
described the gunfights and gambling. No wonder parents
didn't want their sons to be exposed to sinning like that.
"I'm duckin' out of the Hallelujah session, and seein' the
sights."

Ed's eyebrows arched. He never thought up any devilment. "You wouldn't!"

"Double dare you to!"

"Dare what?" Jim asked, straining to hear.

"Mind your beeswax, buttinsky," Billy answered, and
began whistling loudly.

At the morning service the boys were made to sit on a
bench in front of their parents. Ed followed the preacher's

every word. Billy watched bugs crawling on the ground, counted the hairs sprouting on his fingers, and waggled his ears. He fished a string out of his pocket and played cat's cradle. He nibbled his fingernails.

He tried to hook his legs around Jim's and yank him off the bench.

Ma thumped him hard between the shoulders. "Behave, young man!"

He tried hiccuping, and got another thump.

Somehow he survived to the closing hymn. The picnic in the grove was all right, although his mother never let him out of her sight. When everyone streamed back to the tent for the Hallelujah session, Billy was frantically trying to think how to cut loose. He was surprised to hear Ed ask, natural as all get-out, "Ma, Billy and I want to set in back with the older boys."

"You can, but not Billy," she answered.

Mr. Masterson pressed her down the aisle. "Can't keep grown boys under your thumb forever, Katie. Leave them be with their friends. Come on now, or you'll miss a front seat by the Glory Rail."

Jim balked. "I'm going with Ed and Billy."

His mother took a firm grip on his arm. "March, young man. And you too, Tommy. Come along, girls."

Ed and Billy slipped onto the bench farthest back.

"You goin' to slip out and see the sights too?" Billy asked.

"Yup. Soon as they start the opening hymn."

Not long after, Billy hissed, "Let's go."

Outside he strode shoulder to shoulder with his oldest brother. Ed was taller, and ambled along. Billy walked as if he had springs in his heels.

From June through September, Douglas Avenue in Wichita thronged with cattlemen and cowboys. The air reeked of thousands of longhorns bedded down while awaiting shipment East. Planked sidewalks and wooden awnings fronted the business establishments. From past noon until four in the morning the batwing doors of the saloons and gamblinghouses seldom stopped swinging. Coarse laughter and song, the clink of glasses, harsh talk, and not infrequently gunshots blasted through many doorways. These, and the street sounds of freighters popping bullwhips over their oxen, wood-hawkers' screechy-wheeled wagons, and the clop-clop of cow ponies were sweet music to the boys' ears.

Billy gawked at the cowboys, tall, long-waisted fellows who sported high-crowned hats and gun holsters. Sacks of Bull Durham bulged their vest pockets. Cigarettes dangled from their lips. Most wore tent-cloth trousers, or those new "Levi's" with the copper-riveted pockets, and blue cotton shirts open at the neck.

Ed peered into a gamblinghouse. He saw green and red glass chandeliers, a mirror-backed bar, and a swarm of men drinking, smoking, and playing cards. "Look 't that! Those men are sinning in broad daylight!"

Billy strained on tiptoes to look over the batwing doors. "They sure are!"

"But Ma said—" Ed blushed. "I don't see no thunderbolt from Heaven knockin' those fellows straight to eternal damnation."

Billy glanced anxiously at the clear blue sky. "No thunderclouds gathering . . . Hey! Let's go inside."

"No!"

"Scaredy cat!"

"Scaredy cat, nothing! You don't see nobody our age in there. We'd get throwed out on our ears." Ed chewed his lips a moment, then exclaimed, "By gum, I know something we can do."

"What?" Billy asked as he hopped alongside Ed's sudden purposeful steps.

"Something I've been tryin' to get up nerve enough to do for a long time."

Ed swung into the Mercantile and slapped a coin on the counter. "Gimme a plug of Star of Virginia," he demanded of a black-aproned clerk. Outside he peeled off the wrapper, bit off one corner, and chewed deliberately. "Tastes kind of licoricey."

Snatching the plug, Billy bit down hard and chewed greedily. When the sharp tobacco flavor puckered his mouth, he spat fulsomely. "Better 'n gum-tree bark." He tongued the plug to one side so it bulged his cheek, and hitched up his trousers. "No use standin' still when we got a whole town for cuttin' capers."

They passed a hardware store and gunsmithy. Billy looked in the dusty window. "Ed, there's one of them new Sharps Big Fifties, the big buffalo gun Kown told us about. That's the kind I aim to have someday."

Ed read the price card. "You'd pay eighty dollars for a gun?"

Just then the worst odor Billy had ever smelled assailed his nostrils. Four shaggy individuals elbowed him and Ed away from the window. Billy glared. After one look in their rheumy eyes, at their verminous hair and bloodstained clothing, he relaxed his clenched fists. So did Ed. These must be buffalo skinners, the grizzled, gut-slitting hide men Kown had warned them never to cross.

The skinners ignored the boys. One pointed at the Sharps on display. "Wild Bill Hickok, he made hisself five thousand dollars this past winter shootin' buffler with a Big Fifty like that!"

Billy gasped. He looked at Ed wildly. "Did he say five thousand dollars?"

"Yeah," Ed answered dazedly.

Billy's eyes crossed from sheer ecstasy. There was that

much money in the world? His blue eyes blazed. He grabbed
Ed's shirt. "If you and me went buffalo hunting, we could
bail Pa out of debt in one year! And we'd have money left
over to—to—to throw all over the place!"

"Aw now, Billy. You got to remember Kown said Hickok
was the top hunter in the business."

Billy bridled. "Well, I ain't exactly a slouch with a rifle.
Heck, Ed, if we only made a thousand between us, that's
twicet more cash money than Pa has ever made."

"Ma would cut up something awful if I left home."

"You're sixteen! You got to fly the nest someday." Then
Billy swallowed further arguments. If it had taken Ed this
long to buy a plug of tobacco, he couldn't be harangued
overnight into leaving home.

The boys moseyed on down the street. When two men
strolled out of a gamblinghouse, they stopped to gape some
more. From their attire Billy guessed these were gamblers.

The men wore hard-topped, round black hats. Their hair
was pomaded and cut above their starched collars. Their
cheeks were shaven, their mustaches waxed. They wore
expensive-looking suits, white shirts, and polished boots.
Billy's eyes were dazzled by their diamond stickpins, gold
watch chains, and flashing rings. They smoked long thin
panatela-type cigars.

No crude chaw bulged their cheeks, Billy noticed. He
stuck his under his tongue.

The gamblers moved on. The batwing doors swung again
and a tall man stepped out. Always keen-eyed, Billy saw the
cowboys lounging against the building nod respectfully.
Two others all set to blast through the doors hopped aside,
fingered their hats, and were careful not to jostle the tall
man.

He wore a soft-brimmed black hat, white shirt, string tie,
black vest with a silver star on it, and black trousers and

boots. His eyes reminded Billy of river ice. He wore gun and cartridge belts across his waist. Two blunt-nosed holsters housed silver-mounted six-guns.

After the City Marshal walked away, Billy exploded, "Who was that?"

A cowpuncher nearby heard the question. "Two-Gun Collins. Mayor hired him to shoot some law and order in this here town. He kilt two men last night."

Billy crooked a finger, dug the chaw out of his mouth and threw it away.

Ed chuckled. "You won't get arrested for chewin' tobacco. Come on."

When they worked their way back to the revival tent, they sat in the family wagon. Ed studied the sky. "Looks like it's cloudin' on the north. Bet we get soaked going home."

Billy didn't hear. Already he was spinning up a bright daydream. Just a few days more and he'd be leaving home. In no time he would work his way West and earn thousands of dollars as a hunter. Then next summer he could return home all decked out in cowboy boots and diamond ring and silver-mounted pistols! What a handsome dog he'd be with a Tonsorial Parlor haircut, and a shave, and a fine cigar clenched between his teeth. No more chaws for him! That was strictly for farmers.

Ed nudged him. "You watchin' that cloud, Billy? It's sure acting queer."

"Aw, let it rain. Cool things off."

A few moments later Ed exclaimed, "Well, I'll be hornswoggled! That cloud dipped toward the ground. It's all gone! You don't suppose it's a tornado?"

Billy listened for a moment. "Naw. I don't hear no roar. Probably a dust devil."

Not long after a rider on a lathered horse pounded up Douglas Avenue. Seeing the wagons and buggies lined around the tent, he wheeled and rode right under the canvas.

"Grasshoppers! Millions of 'em! Git backfires burnin' before they strip everything!" Then he backed his horse out of the tent, slapped reins, and rode off to spread the alarm further.

The Salvation sermon was forgotten. Farmers and their families rushed outside. Dust boiled high as rig after rig bolted away. The Mastersons tumbled into their wagon, and fought for a place in the line crossing the bridge leading out of town. Mr. Masterson put leather to the team. They raced northward.

After five miles the family saw the forward onslaught of the grasshoppers. Acre after acre was crawling with them. Cornstalks and wheat and barley fell under their attack. Every blade of grass, every weed and flower disappeared. The wagon slithered, crushing thousands crawling over the road. In some fields men, women, and children were beating about futilely with brooms and cloths. Some were lighting backfires. At times the setting sun was blotted out as swarms whirled skyward, circled, and swooped down to devour fresh green acres.

The horses were played out by the time the Masterson homestead was in sight. When they felt the reins slacken, they slowed. They couldn't know that there was no need to hurry now. The farm was already devastated.

Billy bit his lips until they bled. "Poor Pa!" All that back-breaking work for nothing. All the high, bright hopes eaten up!

"We can't leave now," he said fiercely to Ed. "We got to stay and help Pa with next year's crop."

He'd rather take a rawhiding than face another year of farming. But his family came first.

2. RITTER PAYS UP

"BILLY, YOU GONE LOCO? YOU'RE CUTTING OUT CORN INSTEAD of weeds!" Ed chided his brother.

Billy straightened his back and wiped his damp forehead on his sleeve. Middays in June were warm. "I just can't take another year of farming. I'm going to run away."

Ed rested his chin on the hoe handle. "I figured you were working up to something."

"I didn't mind staying the year after the grasshoppers took the crop. But what good did it do? Hail flattened the wheat and stripped the corn, and Pa ended up poor as ever. And last year it was the drought. Now we got this year coming up, and it'll probably be the same old story."

Ed looked out over the greening acres. "It always looks so pretty and promising in the spring."

Billy poked disgustedly at a sturdy weed. "Oh, this is a good enough farm, I s'pose, but it will never support our big family. We'd be doing the folks a favor by leaving."

"But what would we do during the summer when there's no hunting? I think we better wait and see Pa through harvest."

20

"No, by thunder!" Billy exploded, slamming his hoe to the ground. "It's now or never for me. If I have to spend another week weeding, I'll—I'll—" He looked around wildly. "I'll go stark, raving crazy. I found out the Santa Fee is paying three dollars a week for track layers. We can trade in our pelts for a rifle and shot and some groceries, and tickets to the railhead. We can work on the railroad until fall, and then sign up with one of the big hunting outfits."

"But s'pose there aren't any railroad jobs left?"

"But, but, but! You can dig yourself a rut with your old *buts*, and bury yourself in it for all I care, but I'm leaving. Tonight! And if you tell Pa on me, I'll never speak to you again!" Billy grabbed his hoe and stomped to the far end of the cornfield.

As he chopped furiously at the weeds, Billy muttered, "I don't have to run away. A man eighteen years old can do as he durn pleases. Sure, I could tell Pa, and say goodbye all around, but I don't want to do it that way. Nellie and Minnie would bawl, and Ma would lecture an hour on avoidin' evil ways, and Jim and Tom would pull a face." Only Pa would understand why his son jumped the fence rather than walk out through an open gate.

That night Billy went to bed early, exhausted by the pace he had set himself so the day would pass quickly. Hours later he wakened and sat up, listening intently. The house was quiet, his father snoring. When he slipped out of bed and pulled on his pants, Ed startled him by getting up too. Billy whispered excitedly, "You're coming with me?"

"Yes—but hurry, before I lose my nerve."

Each rolled his scant spare clothing in a quilt and, boots in hand, tiptoed to the kitchen. After stuffing a flour sack with cheese and bread, they eased out the door, laced on their boots, and walked to the barn. They gathered up the pelts and hides of the late spring's hunting and swung the packs on their backs. Walking shoulder to shoulder, they crossed the yard, climbed the fence, and headed down the lane that hitched onto the main road to Wichita. It meant walking eighteen miles southward, when their goal lay north and west along the big bend of the Arkansas River to the buffalo country.

At Wichita they traded their pelts for a secondhand Springfield rifle, ammunition, long-handled frying pan, some flour, coffee, salt and soda, side pork, sirup, and tinned tomatoes. From Wichita they hiked twenty-five miles north to Newton and bought tickets to the westernmost point on the Atchison, Topeka and Santa Fe Railroad.

Before the pot-stacked locomotive and string of wooden coaches screeched to a halt at Newton, Billy started running alongside, anxious to be the first to board. No matter that this was the first train he had seen. Time enough later on to get out and really gawk around when the train stopped for water or fuel. He champed at the bit while a few passengers detrained, then leaped up the steps, entered the first coach, slammed his pack under a wood-slatted seat, and sat down. Heart racing, fingers pinched white on the pasteboard ticket, nose pressed against the dirty window, he waited breathless for the train to start.

Ed joined him, but first looked over the sooty benches, the oil lamps suspended from the ceiling, the coal stove at the far end, the baggage partially blocking the aisle or strung overhead in string hammocks. He smiled at the other passengers before sitting beside his brother.

Billy turned, frowning, "What's holding them up?"

Just then the conductor shouted "Bo-o-o-ard!" The locomotive bell clanged. The train got under way with a jolt that almost snapped Billy's head off. He looked out the window and waved gleefully at the loafers leaning against the red station. The train lunged ahead in sharp jolts, and finally attained a rattling speed of twenty-five miles an hour. Houses, gardens, pastures streaked by at a dizzying pace. Billy laughed excitedly. "Hey, we're flying!"

"Tickets!"

Ed nudged Billy. Both handed their pasteboard tickets to the conductor, who punched holes in them and stuck them back in their hatbands.

"How long before we get to the end of the line?" Billy asked.

"Sometime tomorrow morning, barring a breakdown," the man answered flatly.

"What's the nearest town?"

"Dodge City." The conductor moved up the aisle.

Dodge City. The words were music to Billy's ears. He had heard plenty about Dodge City from the tanner's apprentice in Wichita. Queen City of the buffalo hunters it was, the roughest, toughest, wildest, shootingest town in the West! Right out in the heart of the buffalo country, astraddle the old Santa Fe trail, it served as headquarters for the big hunting outfits and their suppliers.

Goodbye, goodbye, Billy's heart sang as the miles slipped past. Goodbye to farming, to family restrictions, to Ma's everlasting sermonizing. Goodbye to poverty, to being a nobody; to having nothing, doing nothing but eat, sleep, and work.

Hello, buffalo country, his heart sang later on. Hello to adventure, excitement, change, challenge. And money. Easy money. Three dollars a week for working no harder than he worked on the farm without pay. And after the big hunt started, maybe a hundred dollars a day. Five thousand in one year! High-heeled boots, a diamond stickpin, silver-handled six-shooters . . . Billy shivered with joy and, from dreaming, slipped into sleep.

"End of the line," the conductor bawled the next morning.

The train began slackening speed. Billy slipped on his

back pack, put the rifle under one arm, and was the first at
the steps. He braced himself as the train came to a shudder-
ing halt out on the prairie. He stepped out into a confusion
of piled-up rails and cedar ties, bales and barrels, tents and
temporary shacks, wagons and teams and laborers. "Where
do you sign up for a job?" he asked a stranger.

"That tarpaper shack on skids," the man answered,
pointing.

"Thanks." Billy saw Ed milling around with the others
pouring off the train. "Ed!" he shouted over the racket,
pointing toward the shack and running. He wanted to be
first in line to sign up for work.

He hopped over the doorsill, hat in hand. He couldn't see
well, coming from glaring sunlight into the cracker-box-sized
office. "Is this where you sign up for jobs?"

"Right here, friend," a man answered from behind a
table made of planks laid on sawhorses.

Billy grinned. The man sounded right friendly. As his
focus sharpened, he saw a red-faced man wearing a too-
tight soiled celluloid collar, checked suit pants and perspiration-soaked shirt, a flashy ring, and a bowler hat set back
off his forehead.

At the same time the man was appraising Billy as another
country bumpkin, raw as a turnip, handsomer than most,
not too tall or beefy, and gullible. "I'm Sam Ritter," he
introduced himself. "I contract with the Santa Fee for clearing and grading the track bed. You interested in work?"

"Yes, sir!"

Ritter checked a chart. "Only thing I got left is sub-
contracting the miles west of Dodge City. You got a
partner?"

"My brother came out with me. He's older. He's a real
good worker."

"Fine!" Ritter answered. "You look like an honest, hard-
working young fellow. You do the job right and I'll do right

by you. You can write the folks you're a subcontractor.
That's a lot better than being a low-down track layer. And
you won't have to live in camp and blow your wages on the
slop they serve up at the railroad commissary. You'll be an
independent businessman, with only me hiring you and a
surveyor checking on you once a week."

"Say, that sounds swell. You won't regret hiring me and
Ed. We'll do a bang-up job for you."

After Ritter had written down their names and signed a
work card for both, he added, "You'll get paid three hundred
dollars for the job. It's got to be finished in two months.
Contact the Santa Fee foreman at Dodge City—that's
thirty-eight miles up ahead—and he'll show you where to
start. Then when you're all through, report to me at the
Dodge House and I'll pay up in cash."

"Yes, sir. Thank you, sir." Billy pocketed the work cards
and left. He found Ed amiably gawking around. "Ed, guess
what? I got us a job. As subcontractors. That's a lot more
important than just being track layers. All we got to do is
clear and grade a mile of roadbed within sixty days, and we
get paid three hundred dollars for it. Three hundred dollars!"

Ed's blue eyes glowed. "You're kidding!"

Handing over the work card, Billy said, "Look there."

"Well, I'll be hornswoggled. . . . When do we start?"

As soon as they contacted the foreman at Dodge City,
Billy explained. "We're subcontracted to do the mile west
of Dodge," he added, making it sound very important.

"Three hundred dollars." Ed shook his head, then shoul-
dered his pack. "Let's get on with it."

Their path led through the squalid tent camp where the
railroad housed the laborers. "Ugh, glad we don't have to
live here." They passed the cook shack where the stench
from piles of rotting garbage turned their stomachs.

The prospects of a fine job and so much money put springs
in their heels. Two days later they walked along Dodge

City's Front Street, abustle with traffic but otherwise peaceful in the morning hours. "Just like Wichita," Billy mentioned as they sought the shade of the wooden awnings strung over the store fronts.

"Yeah, only smaller."

With Billy asking questions they soon located the construction foreman, received exact instructions on where to begin work, and learned they must each pay out a dollar for a shovel.

"You think this shovel is made out of gold?" Billy objected to the storekeeper. But it was a case of pay the price or work empty-handed. "That leaves us only thirty-four cents," Billy fumed. "And we got to live almost two months and buy more supplies." He chewed his lip, then grabbed his shovel and raced out the door. Outside he looked up and down the street, spotted a meat market and made a beeline for it. The butcher was breaking out a hind quarter of buffalo meat.

"You pay cash for fresh-killed meat?" Billy blurted out.

The man laid down the meat ax. "I got meat runnin' out o' my ears." He studied Billy a moment. "Where you working?" After Billy told him their problem, he said, "Maybe you can sell meat to the men working out your way." He turned back to his butchering.

Billy's spirits soared again. He rejoined Ed on the boardwalk. "We're all set."

By evening the two had set up camp at the point where they were to start work. From a nearby dry creek they hacked enough brush to build a wickiup for shelter, smoothed ground for comfortable sleeping space, and put rabbit meat to browning in the skillet. The next morning they began work, breaking the stubborn sod from dawn to dark, raising a track bed and leveling it to the specifications checked on daily by a surveyor. On Sundays they did their laundry, went hunting, swapped or sold venison, ducks, and antelope meat to the workers who brawled Saturdays in Dodge City's saloons and were too weary to hunt for themselves.

Finally their job was completed and the foreman scribbled a note to Ritter, stating that the work was satisfactory. "You'll have to present this before Ritter will pay off," the man told them.

"Come on, let's head for the Dodge House," Billy told Ed.

"Aren't you going to wash up first?"

"Not me! After Ritter pays us I'm headin' straight for Wright and Beverly's and buy me new clothes from the skin out, including a beaded buckskin shirt. Then I'm going to have a hot bath and shave and haircut at the Tonsorial Parlor. And when I come out of there smelling like a lilac, I'm going to Kelley's and order a steak as thick as my wrist."

"You live that high on the hog and you'll be broke inside a week."

Billy looked at his ragged clothes and calloused hands, and answered a little grimly, "Not me." The long grueling work had thinned him down until he was all bone and sinew, and sun-blackened; his hair and soft beard were gray with dust.

The two walked straight to the Dodge House and inquired for Mr. Ritter.

"He checked out," the clerk told them.

"He what?"

"Turned in his key four days back. Said his contract was all done, the railroad paid off, and he was headin' back to Kansas City."

Ed was puzzled. "You don't think Ritter skipped out so he wouldn't have to pay us?"

"What else!" Billy roared, rage knotting his stomach. "We've been bilked. Do I have to draw you a picture?" His fists knotted, and his face purpled. "If I could lay my hands on that thieving varmint, I'd—"

Ed pulled on his arm. "What's done is done. Come on."

Outside, Billy strode up to the timber supporting the wooden awning and butted it with his fists until they bled. Ed waited until Billy's rage cooled, then said, "We got just enough money to pay our fare home. Let's go back, Billy. I know how badly you wanted that money, but I'm glad we're through. I'm so durn homesick I can't stand it much longer."

Billy whirled around. "No, by hang! Ritter will be back. The railroad is pushing through to Granada. He's going east to wangle more contracts, or I'll eat my hat. I'm staying right here. When he shows his face, I'll get our three hundred or plug him full of holes!"

"Now, Billy—" Ed cautioned, though he realized his brother meant every word. "Gosh, I hate to leave you out here alone. What will you do?"

"Don't you worry about me!"

The two returned to their camp and packed their meager belongings, then Ed walked the few miles to the railhead east of Dodge City. Billy rustled a job and a team and wagon from Tom Nixon, who had a lively feed and grain business. When Nixon heard how Ritter had cheated the Masterson boys, he told Billy, "Fix yourself a place to sleep in the granary. If you tell Ed Kelley, he'll probably swap you three meals a day for doing odd jobs around the place."

With his first pay Billy bought a six-shooter and ammunition, and spent an hour daily practicing a fast draw and target shots. He had told everyone who would listen how Ritter had cheated him. As his skill with the revolver increased, he boasted, "If you want to see some fun, just let me know when Ritter is coming through. I'll make him sorry he ever cheated a Masterson!"

Some weeks later the tracks were laid through and beyond Dodge City. The train made regular stops at the new red water tank. Not too long afterward Nixon told Billy, "I heard Ritter is coming through on the train tomorrow."

The next afternoon when the train pulled into the station, Billy jumped aboard. He strode grim-faced through the cars until he spied Ritter. Before he recognized Billy, the contractor found a revolver barrel punched uncomfortably hard in his chest. He looked up into eyes the color of river ice. "What's the meaning of this?"

"Remember me?" Billy said through clenched teeth. "Billy Masterson? You offered to pay me and my brother three hundred dollars for grading the mile west of Dodge. Thought you were smart, duckin' out early so you wouldn't have to pay us?" Billy rammed the gun deeper against Ritter's ribs. "Now you march out onto that platform. I'm going to kill you, Ritter, but I'm going to do it where it won't mess up this car!"

"Help! I'm being robbed!" Ritter appealed to the passengers.

No one in the coach moved. Shaking, whey-faced, Ritter marched through the car to the platform. He didn't realize that the crowd closing in around the car had come to see Billy Masterson make a welsher pay up. "Help! I'm being robbed!"

The bystanders laughed. "Serves you right if he plugs you full of holes, yuh durn no-good cheater!"

Billy said loudly so all could hear, "I'm only asking for what you owe Ed and me. Now hand over three hundred dollars or—"

"I'll pay!" Ritter hauled out a roll of bills and peeled off three hundred dollars.

Billy took the money, backed down the steps, and stuck the gun in his waistband. The bystanders greeted him with a glad shout, hoisted him on their shoulders, and carried him to Kelley's saloon. Billy laughed, and waved the money for all to see.

"Buy us a drink, Billy! Celebrate!"

"Sure, set 'em up," Billy told the bartender grandly. He wanted to celebrate, to treat all the good fellows who had backed him up. It made him feel important, having all that money to spend. When the bartender shoved a drink at him, he hesitated for a moment. But when he saw the others around him, glasses raised, waiting for him, he downed the liquor in one long swallow. With all the shouting and back-slapping, few noticed him gasp, wheeze, shudder, and fight for breath.

"You really buffaloed Ritter," his new pals kept congratulating him. "How about celebratin' with another round, Billy?"

"Sure, sure!"

Tom Nixon drifted into the saloon. "Have a drink on me," Billy offered.

Nixon laid a hand on his shoulder. "You get out of here before these no-good bums drink up every cent you took off Ritter. Take your money over to Wright and Beverly's and have them put it in the safe, where no one can borrow off you until you're broke."

Billy's temper flared for a second. What right had Nixon coming in here, spoiling his fun? But then he looked down at the money clenched tightly in his left hand. It wasn't all his money. Half belonged to Ed. Maybe he had better leave now. "Sorry, fellas," he called out. "See you later. The boss just cracked the whip. I got to get back to work."

In spite of the crowd's urging him to stand for one more round, Billy slipped out. He ran all the way to the post office and mailed a hundred and fifty dollars to Ed, then placed the remainder of his share in the store safe. That was the place for it until hunting season.

3. FIRST HUNT

In September, Billy observed hunters drifting in—purposeful, clear-eyed men in contrast to the feisty skinners who had loafed and brawled all summer. The Rath, Mooar, Myers, and Wright stores buzzed with hunt preparations. Brashly confident, Billy sought one outfit after another for a job as hunter.

"Experience?" he was asked.

"None, but I've been hunting since I was eight."

Mostly he was told, "Git along, greenhorn." There were a few offers of jobs as camp boy.

"Nothing doing." William Barclay Masterson wasn't going out on a hunt to rustle firewood and scour pots!

By chance he learned that some Dodge City merchants would grubstake hunters in return for a percentage of their hide sales. "How about it?" he asked his boss.

Nixon laughed. "You don't know straight up about the business."

Billy shrugged. After several more refusals he approached Bob Wright, former freighter and hunter, now partner in Wright and Beverly, the largest supplier in Dodge City.

"Experienced?" Wright asked him, noting his youthful appearance.

The question was beginning to annoy Billy. "No, but I'm a crack shot and—"

Wright walked away to wait on others at the counter.

Billy jammed his thumbs under his belt, and shouted, "How is a man to prove himself if nobody will listen to him?"

"Maybe you'd better pull your sights down a little, greenhorn."

Billy looked sharply at a lean black-haired man clad in smoked buckskins and moccasins, his hair and beard glossily clean. "Aw, what do you know about it?"

The stranger took a dried prune from a barrel and chewed on it. "The question is, what do you know about hunting buffalo?"

"I'll match shots with anyone in the business!"

"Every fresh-faced kid who comes West claims to be a crack shot. What experience have you had fighting Indians?"

"What's that got to do with it?"

Behind long bronzed fingers pressed against his lips to keep from laughing, the man said, "Quite a bit, which you would know if you did less talking and more listening."

Billy's eyebrows shot up; his eyes darkened. "I've listened plenty, and there ain't an Indian living can make me back-water!" He had heard the talk about the big hunt likely being down along the Salt Fork of the Arkansas, hunting ground treatied to the Indians and supposedly forbidden to white hunters. The Kiowas and Cheyennes were sure to raise a fuss, but they would be run down by a swarm of well-armed hunters. Not hundreds; thousands would be hunting this winter of 1872–73 because a bad depression, unemployment, and drought back East had resulted in a stampede to the buffalo country. The hide business was about the only lucrative thing a poor man could break into.

Just then Wright called to the man, "Your wagons are all set, Dixon."

Billy gulped. Dixon! This fellow who had been baiting him was Billy Dixon, one of the greatest hunters in the business. Dixon's exploits as a scout, Indian fighter, and hunter were common talk around Dodge. An odd fellow in some ways, not yet twenty-five, didn't drink or smoke or chew, never swore, never caroused, never turned a gun in anger on a white man but was sure death to buffalo and attacking Indians. Billy blurted, "I guess I did mouth off like a fresh-faced kid, Mr. Dixon." But his blue eyes blazed as he added, "But I know what I can do with a rifle, and I'm going to prove it if I have to go out alone!"

Dixon had been studying Billy as they stood side by side at the counter. He saw in his face and hands evidence of his outdoor labor, his lean toughness, even sensed the rocklike determination masked by a cockiness that wasn't all brag. The lad was right. How could he prove himself if no one gave him the chance? "Would you like to throw in with my outfit?"

"Holy smokes, yes!" Billy almost shouted. "You really mean it?"

Dixon nodded. "Get yourself some warm clothing. Be at my camp at the east fording before daylight." He started to leave.

"I—I don't have a Sharps," Billy added quickly.

Dixon looked puzzled a moment, then smiled. "You won't need one."

"Don't you want to know my name? I'm Billy Masterson."

"So long, Masterson."

Billy's heart began to pound. What luck! Of course Dixon knew a good man when he saw one. That's why he offered him a job. With his chest puffing out like a pouter pigeon's, Billy called to Wright, "How about a little service here?"

At four the next morning, his belongings stuffed in a grain sack, Billy set out for the hunters' camp. He arrived just as the outfit was lining out to ford the Arkansas: six wagons, tongue and trailer units hitched together and drawn by horses; a single wagon loaded with water barrels, tarps, camping gear, ammunition, and food. He counted fourteen men, excluding himself, all mounted.

"Toss your gear aboard and grab a horse," Dixon ordered.

Shivering more from the excitement than the clammy mist smudging the countryside, Billy humped to it. There was no talk. Dixon was slipping across the river before the myopic patrol from nearby Fort Dodge made a feeble pass at keeping the hide men from crossing the Deadline, the Arkansas River, into the hunting paradise forbidden them by treaty. At daylight Dixon's wagons had topped the first line of sand hills on the south, and dropped from sight of the sentries.

When they stopped briefly at mid-morning for coffee, cold meat, and biscuit, a thousand questions popped in Billy's mind. He held his tongue, rather than expose himself as a rank greenhorn. Watching the others, he picketed his horse on the grass. Only Dixon was wearing buckskins and moccasins, the others favoring wool pants and shirts, soft-brimmed hats and boots as Billy did. The looks raked his way made him feel he was being gone over with a lice-catcher. Too awed to strike up a conversation with the hunters, he looked sharp for a way to be helpful.

"Want some help?" he asked Flapjack Flaherty. It never hurt to be on the pie side of the cook.

Flaherty, a hollow-chested man whose walrus mustache ends dropped onto his shirt, pinioned Billy with a glance as sharp as a buffalo-berry thorn. "Y're right. Git a fire goin'."

For a split second Billy wanted to remind Flapjack, "You can't talk to me like that. I'm one of the hunters." But he didn't want to have trouble right off. He scooped a fire pit, started a blaze with dry grass and buffalo chips and, when shown the mess kit, set out mugs and the sugar can.

Among the men there was as yet none of the friendly joshing back and forth which Billy expected. That would come later. Now all but Dixon were warily friendly but watchful, like a pack of strange dogs coming together for the first time.

At sunset Dixon circled his wagons beside a grove along a creek bottom. He ordered grass cut so the horses need not be turned out for night grazing and thus fall prey to Indians prowling in the hills. While riding from the prairie upland down to the creek, Billy had spotted deer in the thickets. Here was a chance to show his stuff. He started loading the Springfield, but Dixon said, "No shooting. Give Flaherty a hand."

Billy helped the cook, though it rankled to be doing menial chores while others lounged around. But he was the new man, and the youngest, and he guessed he'd have to put up with some unpleasantness, if only to prove he was a good guy. After a rib-busting meal of fried ham, skillet bread and gravy, tinned peaches and coffee, lye-strong and nicely gritty with grounds, the fire was doused and blankets laid out under the wagons. There was no talking and no smoking after dark. Sounds carried miles across the prairie after the wind died down.

Billy rolled in his blanket, wormed a comfortable place for his hip bones, and relaxed to the night sounds: the familiar ones of horses cropping grass nearby, the light keening prairie breeze, a far-off coyote howling up the moon. Before long he heard the rise and fall of the men's snoring, mostly a gentle growling, though one sounded like a buzz saw bucking through cottonwood. Suddenly Billy began to chuckle, but covered his mouth. All the precautions of no fire and no talking so as not to toll the Indians to their camp, and nothing done about telltale snoring that surely could be heard for miles!

Late afternoon of the third day Billy got his first look at the great Arkansas herd. East, south, and west the plain was black with buffalo—grazing, grunting, their backs glistening like a dark ocean, clouds of dust swirling around those wallowing in the dirt.

When Dixon stopped his wagons some three miles north and up wind from the herd, Billy glanced behind them. Like the ribs of a fan, outfits were stringing in from all directions. He became so excited he shivered like a wet dog. His fingers itched for a gun. How could he possibly wait until morning to hunt?

"Git off yore hunkers and git to work, you fresh-faced blankety-blank wet ear!"

Billy vaulted from the saddle and picketed his horse. Flapjack tolerated no arguing. Only the thought that tomorrow he would be hunting and out from under Flapjack's constant do-this, do-that, kept Billy from jawing back at the cook.

When he lay in his blanket Billy heard a rough, steady, low-keyed thunder, the wind-borne sound of a million buffalo mouths tonguing the tough grass from its roots. He grinned. It was such a prosperous sound, assuring a man of a hundred-dollar-a-day kill. He drifted off to sleep before he could think up half enough wonderful ways to spend all the money he would be making.

The sky was barely paling in the east when Billy wakened. He sat up, digging the sleep out of his eyes. At home he preferred the earliest hours for hunting, but here no one was stirring.

Dixon nearby opened one eye. "Anything wrong?"

"No. Isn't it time to get up?"

Dixon grunted and shut his eye.

Billy started to lie down but stopped when a wonderful

idea hit him. He would sneak out and kill his first buffalo before the others were even awake. He flung back the covers and started pulling on his boots when Dixon ordered, "Go back to sleep."

"Yes, sir," Billy answered.

After breakfast he stood around, waiting to be assigned a big-caliber rifle and ammunition belt. The hunters stomped off, arguing where they would make their first stand. The skinners whetted their knives. "What do I do?" Billy asked Dixon.

"You're camp boy. You follow the skinners. Soon as they've got a hide skinned, peg it out fur side up for drying. See you don't soldier on the job."

Camp boy! Billy's dream of hundred-dollar-a-day earnings shattered. He wasn't even going to have a chance to show what a good hunter he was. He gritted his teeth and clenched his fists. For two cents he'd walk off—

Oh no, he wouldn't. He'd stick it. Wait his chance. He'd show 'em all!

He hated the job. As soon as the stinking, lice-ridden bloody hide was ripped off the dead buffalo, and the carcass blazed gory and greasy in the harsh sunlight, Billy had to roll the hide fur side out, lug it to camp, and peg it out to dry. He had done his share of butchering on the farm, but nothing like this. Across the three miles separating the camp from the herd, the mellow boom of the Sharps and the sharper popping of heavy-caliber Springfields dinned in his ears. And me pegging hides! he thought disgustedly, hating it more and more.

That wasn't all he disliked. He took a violent and enduring dislike to the skinners, though he was careful not to show it. How any human beings could wallow so in filth and lice, could ignore soap and comb and match their language to their own stink appalled him. He expected to be dirty; a man didn't work outdoors without picking up mud, dust, and what-all. But there was always a bucket of hot water for washing, if he saw to it, and a change of shirt and socks if he wasn't above doing his own laundry. And Billy wasn't.

The skinners needled him about his cleanliness day after day, trying to prod him into a fight. Dirty-Nose Charlie became so insulting that suddenly Billy piled into him, fighting hard like a wildcat. Not because he was afraid he might be beaten. Far from it! The sooner the fight was over, the sooner he would be free of bodily contact with the skinner; the sooner he could delouse; the sooner he would have proved he was a cougar in a fight and a good man to leave be. He and Dirty-Nose punched, grunted, rolled in the dirt, pummeled each other. Billy saw his chance and butted Dirty-Nose hard on the chin with his head. The skinner fell senseless to the dirt. Billy staggered to his feet, wiped his bleeding nose, and dared those ringed about him, "Anybody else wants to call me names better get it out of his system right now."

The skinners laughed good-naturedly. "You're all right, Billy. No hard feelings."

Sometime later when the itch to fire a gun became intolerable, Billy said half-sarcastically to Dixon, "Long as I'm considered too green to handle a rifle, mind if I do a little target shooting with my six-gun?"

"I'll match you," Dixon offered, much to Billy's surprise.

They walked off from the wagons, stood stock-still until the prairie dogs that had streaked down their holes began popping up again. With his six-gun Dixon killed several as the little animals darted about in lightninglike streaks. Billy was awkward and slow on the draw, and only fair at shooting.

"You plan to circulate around Dodge and keep company with hide outfits?" Dixon asked after a bit.

"I plan to be a hunter if I ever get the chance. Why?"

"A man as slow as you on the draw won't last long."

"I don't plan to have trouble with anybody."

Dixon grunted. "I've watched you for some time now, Billy. You and trouble are natural first cousins." He didn't elaborate on this, but went on to say, "Keep practicing with that waist gun, hear? I'll furnish the ammunition."

With that, Dixon returned to camp. Billy was puzzled. There was no reason for Dixon to take an interest in a green kid; but if Dixon said to practice, he would. He had looked upon his six-gun as something for amusement. Maybe he had better sharpen up. In Dodge the soldiers from the fort grudge-fought with the skinners; the bullwhackers jawed with the mule skinners; everybody scrapped with the railroad workers. Bad whisky flowed faster than the Arkansas. Someone was always pulling a gun. Already twenty-five men had been shot down and buried on the hill north of town. The more he thought about it, the more merit Billy saw in Dixon's advice.

When two thousand hides were ready for marketing, Dixon sent the wagons to Dodge. Since Billy could read and write, and the wagonmen could not, Dixon sent him along to transact some business and buy supplies at Wright's. "Draw some of your pay, if you want."

Billy thought fast. "Could I have eighty dollars?"

Dixon wrote out the order against the cash he banked at Wright's.

Eighty dollars was nothing compared to what he had hoped to earn, but it would buy a fifty-caliber Sharps buffalo gun. As Billy figured on the long ride to and from camp, somehow he'd wangle a day's shooting. Once Dixon saw how many buffalo he could bring down, William Barclay Masterson would be through forever with being a lowly camp boy.

On returning to the Salt Fork of the Arkansas, Billy learned a small outfit comprised of a hunter and three skinners had thrown in with Dixon's camp. "How come?" he asked Flapjack.

"Injuns."

Reason enough, Billy figured. The newcomers stayed separate, cooking and sleeping by their own fire.

As usual after supper and chores, Billy walked off by himself to practice with his six-gun. Since Dixon had turned down his request to hunt, Billy didn't want his company. He was plenty burned up, and vented his spleen in rough shooting. As he stood slightly spraddle-legged, jerking the gun out of the holster, someone said quietly, "Turn your wrist and lift up on it."

Billy looked up at a tall, light-haired man he figured was some five or six years his senior. There was such a quiet authority in the stranger's voice that Billy answered, "All right." After several tries he noted that turning his wrist slightly did quicken his draw some. "Thanks for the tip. Like to match shots?"

The stranger nodded, drew, and shot a prairie dog so swiftly that Billy's jaw sagged. "How'd you ever learn to shoot that good?"

"Practice," was the simple answer.

"Would you give me some more pointers?"

"Learn to point by instinct. If you haven't that born in you, you'll never be an expert with a six-gun."

Billy fired several shots.

"Steady. Don't try to show off. The speed comes with practice."

"Yes, sir," Billy said meekly.

"Temper and a gun are natural enemies. Every time you unholster that gun be sure you're steady, mentally unflustered. *Mentally deliberate but muscularly faster than thought.* Understand what I mean?"

"I'm trying to," Billy said, repeating the advice. "Say, I'm

drawing and shooting better already. I sure do thank you."
He extended his hand. "My name is Billy Masterson."

"Wyatt Earp," the other responded. Since it was now too
dark to continue, he said, "See you tomorrow."

Back at his camp, Billy asked Cranky McCabe, one of the
hunters, "You know that Earp fellow?"

"Some. One of the best hunters out here, but quiet—awful
quiet. Don't mix. Don't drink. No brag to him."

"I noticed he's got good horses and equipment. Gosh, I'm
just a greenhorn with a six-gun; but he sure went to a lot of
trouble tonight showing me how to speed up my draw.
Can't imagine why."

McCabe rarely smiled, but this time he grinned. "You're
a friendly pup, Billy. If you barked, he'd probably scratch
yore ears."

Unable to figure out whether McCabe was compliment-
ing or insulting him, Billy went to bed. He had two more
sessions with Earp before the hunter turned his loaded
wagons toward Dodge. "See you," Earp said in farewell.

"I sure hope so!" Billy called after him.

When Dixon, his hunters and skinners left camp around
ten that morning, and only Flapjack was around, Billy
filled his pants pockets with three-inch cartridges, shoul-
dered the new Sharps, and took off in an easterly direction—
away from the main hunt. Chances of an Indian attack were
greater that way, but he threw caution to the winds. It was
now or never.

"Come back here and fill the water barrel," Flapjack
hollered.

"Go to blazes!" Billy bawled back, and loped across the
prairie.

Five miles out he had the prairie and the herd to himself,
the big hunt being on the north and west flanks of the herd.
He hadn't seen hide nor hair of an Indian. With so many

hunters in the area they had probably all turned tail anyway. When he dropped down into a creek drainage crowded with buffalo, he sucked in his breath. This was it!

He moved forward bent-kneed, staying upwind. Hunters who used Sharps preferred to hunt from five to seven hundred yards. Not he! He tested the sights, lowered them for two hundred yards, and moved in closer. He'd gamble on what hunters told him: that the buffalo, in spite of the slaughter, had not yet learned to be wary of a man on foot. He picked a fat cow for his first shot, aimed, and fired; moved the barrel slightly and fired again, and again and again. Then he crouched, waiting for the barrel to cool; panting, his blood pounding, his heart hammering. He just couldn't miss! The dying animals slumped to their knees while the others spooked off a short distance, then settled down to graze again. What stupid animals!

For hours Billy ran to different firing positions, heedless of getting farther and farther from camp. No matter. The devil with watching for Indians! He had no time for screwing his neck in six directions.

When forty-seven carcasses lay motionless, their blood soaking the grass, Billy called it quits. His trigger finger was blistered, his shoulder pummeled raw from the kickback. He started for camp, not too weary to imagine how he would bowl Dixon over with the news of his first day's tally. Pretty good for a beginner. If Dixon fired him for refusing to continue as camp boy, he'd just sashay over to the next camp. Forty-seven kills in one day should get him on as hunter anywhere. He patted the Sharps satisfyingly.

Head in the clouds, eyes seeking out the camp where he would make his brag, Billy plowed on across the prairie, down across the brush-choked wash of a dry creek and up the shallow bank.

A blow on the head knocked him flat. Before he could turn, he was grabbed from behind. He struggled furiously but in vain. Two Indians, one on each side, pinned his arms back until he had to quiet down or have them broken. A third rammed a lance at his side, drawing blood, while another quickly stripped him of his knife and waist gun. The fifth scooped up the Sharps and slammed the barrel against the side of his head. Billy dropped like a stone.

When he regained consciousness, his head throbbed so he couldn't believe his skull could hold so much pain. He struggled to his feet and looked blearily around. Not an Indian in sight! Then rage hit hard, making his head throb even more. He was furious at being overtaken, robbed without a fair chance to fight back. No matter that his brashness was to blame. Gritting his teeth, he headed for Dixon's camp.

Dixon spotted him and walked out to meet him. "What happened?"

Still so mad he could hardly talk, Billy spat out a brief account and then made a beeline for the horses.

"What do you think you're going to do?" Dixon demanded.

"I'm going to trail those thievin' Indians back to their camp and have it out with them! They're not taking a Sharps off of me without hearing from me!"

Dixon stopped him with a strong arm. "You trying to commit suicide? Count yourself lucky to be alive. Over two hundred Kiowas hit the camps around here late this morning. I lost two skinners. Some of the smaller outfits were wiped out. We're packing up and heading for Dodge right now. For all we know, the plain will be swarming with Indians before nightfall."

Billy forgot his aches and pains. He helped break camp, saddled his horse and rode alongside the creaking wagons as they headed north. The longer he rode under the darkening sky, the madder he got. He had been cheated, robbed, whopped on the head. He wanted revenge, one way or another. But how?

He set to thinking. From what Dixon and the others said, the Indians had struck from the northwest. Dodge lay north-northeast and the wagons would roll all night.

Billy waited until after the first stop to rest and water the horses. Then, mounted and armed with the Springfield, he peeled off in the dark. He kept his bearings by the North Star. Repeatedly he stopped to listen and smell. Just as the darkness was beginning to bleach, he caught the scent of a horse herd. He picketed his mount and cautiously moved forward on foot. Not far ahead in a low swale he spotted a fair-sized pony herd. On hands and knees he crept closer. Where were the guards?

He froze. There they were, two of them, hunkered down before a tiny fire. He inched forward soundlessly, then swiftly rose to his feet and ran down on them swinging the rifle butt savagely from side to side. The guards toppled without even shouting an alarm.

Billy turned and raced for his horse, mounted and rode at an angle so he came up on the herd from the south. The lead mare lifted her head sharply, and began moving west. Billy toed his horse and cut her off. She turned northeast and Billy slowed. He didn't want the herd stampeding. No telling whether they would ride over the Indian camp or not.

But luck was with him. By sunrise he sighted Dixon's wagons, yahooed, and closed the distance between them.

Dixon was speechless, seeing Billy and the herd, but the skinners slapped him on the back and allowed "even Hickok hisself couldn't match what you done, Billy boy!" Yes sir, when they got to Dodge and spread the word, he'd be famous—a hero, a legend!

Billy soaked up their flattery. Skinners weren't such bad fellows after all. "Thanks, fellas. I'll pay five dollars a piece to whoever helps me drive these ponies to the horse market at Dodge. And free drinks afterward if I make a good sale!"

The trader at Dodge paid Billy twelve hundred dollars in

exchange for forty sound Indian ponies. Billy paid off his helpers and told them, "Hit for Kelley's, boys, and start celebrating! I'll be along after a bit."

The skinners whooped and raced for the saloon. Although bursting with pride and anxious to tell his story to any or all who would listen, Billy rode first to Wright's. He exchanged the soiled money for gold certificates, banked three hundred dollars in the safe, and mailed three hundred to his father.

Twelve hundred dollars is pretty good return for two stolen guns and a lump on the head, he chortled as he headed for a whapdoodle of a splurge.

4. SIEGE AT ADOBE WALLS

FOR EIGHTEEN MONTHS BILLY'S LIFE FOLLOWED A PATTERN of hunting buffalo with one outfit after another, piling up good earnings and squandering them in splurges of one sort or another. Although he missed Ed, he had no desire to go home. Infrequent letters told him life on the farm was improving some. The money he sent home was used for improvements and to buy more land. "We all miss you," Ed wrote. "Pa wishes you would come home and give him a hand with the crops."

"Not me!" Billy exclaimed. He'd never do another day's farming if he lived to be a hundred.

When Billy and Dixon joined Brick Bond's big hunting outfit, the hunters taught Billy how to play faro and poker. The lessons came high; he rarely won. "So I'm broke again," he'd say, laughing, after he paid his debts. There was always another hunt ahead, and promise of more money. Next to guns he found he liked cards best, liked studying men's faces as they played, liked the nice suspense as each card was turned up, even liked quietly observing how men cheated.

He had never forgotten the first gamblers he had seen, at Wichita. Even though he could have afforded it, he held off buying an expensive suit and flashy ring. He would get the hunting out of his system first, learn all the tricks pulled on greenhorns and suckers, and then swap a Sharps, bedroll, and coarse woolens for silver-mounted pistols, a feather tick in a high-class boardinghouse, and clothes fit for a king.

And why not be a gambler? It was a respectable profession on the frontier. A gambler was looked upon as any other businessman, even envied by those who were badgered by freight costs, slow-moving stock, indifferent clerks, fire, theft, and myriad other problems. Or a depression, such as Dodge was feeling these days.

By March, 1874, when he was twenty, so many millions of buffalo had been slaughtered and the prairie hundreds of miles around Dodge City so shot clean that the Queen City of the buffalo hunters suffered a tight squeeze. The huge ricks and hide warehouses along the railroad were empty, the skinners broke, outfitters' shelves groaning with unpurchased supplies. The only herd left was south of the Canadian River in Comanche country, too far from Dodge or the protection of the fort.

Then one of the merchants, Charlie Myers, had an idea. "I'll set up a trading post and build a stockade down on the Canadian if you hunters will go down there with me. I'll even pay you to freight my stuff so your wagons won't roll empty."

The idea caught fire. Charlie Rath and the Mooar brothers agreed to establish stores at the post, and Emanuel Dubbs too. Jim Hanrahan said he'd open a saloon if he had any whisky left to sell by the time they all got down there. Mr. and Mrs. William Olds would set up a restaurant, and

O'Keefe, the blacksmith, figured to move lock, stock, forge, and bellows. Dodge came to life overnight as hunters outfitted, merchants loaded long lines of wagons; horses, oxen, and mules churned the mud on Front Street.

"You interested?" Dixon asked Billy when they heard about the new venture.

Billy turned his empty pockets inside out. "I'll say. I'm busted flat." And he had thought he knew all the tricks! He had got into a hot game at Kelley's with some big-time gamblers fresh out of Kansas City. He was raking in the chips, all guyed up because he was stripping these fellows, when they tossed their diamond stickpins into the pot. It took every one of Billy's chips to cover that raise. Then the gamblers threw in their diamond rings. Trying to bluff me out of several thousand dollars, eh? Billy figured to himself. Well, I'll show them! He wrote an IOU for every dollar he had in Wright's safe, and called the bet. Then he laid down four queens. "Let's see you beat that!"

"Four kings," one of the gamblers said quietly, and added, "I trust you can cover that IOU, Masterson."

Though stunned, Billy's ears were tuned to the icy threat underlying the gentlemanly question. "I'll be back in five minutes with the money."

"My friend will go with you," the gambler offered silkily.

Billy rose slowly, his blue eyes darkening with rage. "You saying I might skip out and welsh on my debt?"

One gambler's fingers were filled with poker chips; the other's reached for a gun hidden in a shoulder holster. Billy outdrew him swiftly. Both gamblers understood six-gun talk. "We'll wait here until you return."

Billy holstered his guns and left Kelley's. He was surprised at himself for drawing a gun on a man; he had never done that before, though he had seen it done many times and frequently with disastrous consequences. But it had proved easy; the bluff had worked. To be honest, he'd much rather have left knuckle-bruises on the gambler's face.

When he returned to pay off the money owed, he acted as if he couldn't care less. But, deep inside, it graveled him. The loss knocked a lot of brag out of him. So when Dixon asked him later if he were interested in hunting along the Canadian, he was.

The next morning Dixon and Billy claimed their horses at the livery stable and joined the crowd jamming Front Street. The townspeople gathered to see the long line of wagons and riders leave, Myers' sheeted wagons leading off, flanked by many of the great names among hunters and skinners: Dixon, Masterson, Dave Mather, Hurricane Bill Martin, Prairie Dog Dave Morrow, Eat-'em-Up Jake, the Hoodoo Kid, Blue Pete, Dirty Face Charlie, Conch Jones, Bullwhack Joe, Shotgun Collins; even Dutch Henry, whose side line was stealing horses. Only Wyatt Earp was missing; he had forsaken hunting for a marshalship in Wichita. All the men were optimistic. They were heading for virgin buffalo-hunting country where a stout stockade and supplies aplenty would be close at hand. Soon wagons piled high with hides would trundle back and forth across the far-flung prairie between the millions of buffalo on the Canadian and the hide buyers at Dodge.

"Prosperity, here we come!" they sang out.

Myers led the way down into the panhandle of Texas and established his post along a creek feeding into the Canadian. It was near the ruins of an abandoned Indian trading post known as Adobe Walls. Forty years earlier the Bent brothers had a flourishing trade center there, but it was a disintegrating ruin now. Ten years back Kit Carson had a narrow squeak at the Walls, and survived an Indian attack only because his opponents lost interest in fighting after sundown and he escaped.

All hands pitched in to help Myers erect a twenty-by-sixty-foot sod building with bastions at opposite corners. They set twelve-foot cottonwood logs three feet deep to form a stout picket corral along the creek. Hanrahan's saloon was equally large and boasted a ridgepole two and a half feet in diameter supporting the roof. The Olds's restaurant did a flourishing business even before walls and roof boxed in the stove and planked tables. With more sod huts to quarter the laborers, hunters, and skinners; the tangle of added corrals bulwarked by wagons, empty only until the hides came pouring in, the men of the new Adobe Walls settlement felt secure enough to hold off the entire Comanche fighting force if need be.

By May the buildings were finished, and a dark smear on the southern horizon tolled the buffalo moving north toward the Canadian. The hunters took off with a whoop and holler, traveling light and fast since scouts reported the region bristling with Indian sign, though not a single red man had been sighted.

Dixon, Billy, and four skinners rode south across the greening tableland and made camp. Hunting was excellent. Billy was full of beans; deadly with his Sharps from morning to mid-afternoon, when he switched to a light shotgun for wild turkey, quail, and prairie chickens for the stew kettle. He gathered tender-leaved lamb's-quarter, welcome addition to a diet largely of starches and meat. The late day hours were lively with card games, fiddling and singing, and target contests. Since Dixon permitted no liquor in camp, his men remained healthy, clear-eyed, and alert. All took turns at round-the-clock guard duty.

Others were not so fortunate. Reckless, greedy, dissolute, they shot a bloody swath through the herd; poked deeper into Indian country and farther from the stockade, tapping the whisky barrels freely. One by one they went down, scalped, mutilated.

Emanuel Dubbs's outfit returned to the Walls with a small

fortune in hides, stocked up on food and ammunition, and headed east. For days his men couldn't shoot and skin fast enough. But one red-streaked dawn the Comanches struck hard. None survived to tell the horror.

When Dixon noted Indian tracks thicker than chicken tracks in a barnyard, he decided, "We'll quit while we still got our hair." Billy and the skinners, edgy from mounting tension and lack of sleep, were agreeable. They made it safely to the Walls by nightfall.

While Dixon dickered with Rath, sold the hides, and paid off the skinners, Billy treated himself to Mrs. Olds's dried peach pie and coffee. Then he moseyed over to Hanrahan's and stacked his Sharps in the corner with many others. The saloon was popping with talk about men killed, narrow escapes, and a possible all-out attack by the Comanches.

"What do you think?" Billy asked when Dixon joined him in the smoky low-ceilinged room.

Dixon shrugged. "Bound to have trouble." He made a face. "Let's get out of here."

As much as Billy liked swapping talk in a crowded saloon, he followed Dixon. The air inside was too strong even for him. Outside, the two strolled up and down in front of the buildings. Mrs. Olds stepped from her doorway, pitcher in hand, and watered a morning-glory vine transplanted from Dodge. "Evening."

"Evening," they answered politely, lifting their hats.

"Sure hot," Billy murmured, wiping his face and neck. He opened his perspiration-soaked shirt and pulled its sticky wetness away from his chest and back.

Dixon nodded silently and moved from the shadows cast by the buildings out into the brilliant moonlight.

Billy looked up at the round, smiling moon. "Bet a fellow could read in this light." When Dixon remained silent, with none of the easy give-and-take between them, Billy said, "Something eating you?"

"Be quiet," Dixon whispered. He walked out from the buildings and corrals, far enough so the noise from Hanrahan's no longer clouded his hearing.

In spite of the heat Billy shivered. He felt so naked out in the bright light, in the unnerving quiet leaking in from the prairie. When an owl hoot drifted across the hot night, every hair on his head prickled. For as long as he could remember, an owl hoot had always spooked him.

An answering owl hoot . . . and after a long silence, another.

Dixon turned back. "Let's turn in."

"Good idea."

They passed Old Man Keeler, long-time Plains hunter, lounging outside Myers' store. "Ever see moonlight bright as this?" Billy commented. "Makes the street almost as bright as the Long Branch saloon in Dodge."

Keeler spat. "Thet's a Comanche moon, Buster. We'll have hell for brekfuss."

Billy snorted. "Our Sharps will teach them a thing or two." Privately he tagged Keeler for a calamity howler. Old men were prone to that.

Inside Hanrahan's the smoke and heat had brought an end to the drinking. Before blowing out the lamps the proprietor called, "Any of you want to bed down in here tonight, go to it."

Some drifted out, the Shadler brothers to their wagon near the corral, others to spread bedrolls in the shadows near the buildings. Billy found an old coat, made up a pillow, and stretched out on the floor. Dixon lay nearby; one of the skinners appropriated a card table and another the top of the bar. One by one the men dropped off to sleep. Only Old Man Keeler hunkered down beside the door, sleepless, waiting.

The moon circled west; dipped behind horsetail clouds; emerged swollen, orange, leering. The heat thinned out and

early-morning coolness freshened even the air inside Hanrahan's. Far to the east the owl hoots died out.

Cr-ack!

The loud noise jarred all awake in the saloon.

"What's goin' on?"

"Light the lamp!"

As men fumbled for trousers and boots, Hanrahan
shouted, "The ridgepole is splitting. Shore it up or we'll be
buried alive."

By match flares Billy and Dixon grabbed their rifles and
supported it until others found a timber long and sturdy
enough to shore up the sagging pole. Those who came
running from other places returned to their blankets.

Inside Hanrahan's the men started to josh one another
about their state of undress. The proprietor glanced outside.
It was getting light. He ought to do a good business in eye
openers. "I'll buy a drink," he shouted. While the others
crowded the bar, Billy went to the stove in the corner and
filled mugs with cold coffee for himself and Dixon. "Never
could see brushing my teeth with whisky," he joked to
his partner.

Dixon was standing by an open window, studying the
eastern horizon. He took the mug, drained it, and handed
it back without turning his head. Billy put down his silence
to early-morning grouchiness; but when he stiffened, Billy
glanced out the window too. He saw a wide dark band come
out of the east, the ends turning in toward the settlement.
"Buffalo!" he exclaimed.

"Buffalo, my foot! It's a big war party!" Dixon shouted the
alarm.

The men at the bar exploded into action. They alerted
those in the other buildings and began a desperate race—
some grabbed rifles and broke out cases of ammunition;
others barricaded the doors and windows with tables, flour
sacks, and bales of hay. In that short time the thunder of

hoofbeats and yowling war whoops beat down on their ears.

Billy grabbed his Sharps and Dixon's, while Dixon tore open a box of cartridges. They punched the glass out of one window, stood back loading calmly while others slapped a barricade of sorts in front of them, then took their stand. There wasn't time to be scared. For the rest of his life Billy would never forget that tidal wave of howling, painted, mounted, armed Comanches pouring down on them.

His eyes lighted; his lips drew back in a wolfish grin; his pulse raced. His gun barked, and Dixon's and others. Warriors plummeted to the ground with each volley, yet swarm upon swarm of bowmen and lancers besieged the soddies. The men in the bastions picked off the first wave of those who leaped for the roofs and corrals, or backed their ponies against the doors and tried to kick in the barriers.

Billy fired and ducked, fired and ducked, aimed at every face and body that crossed his sights. He was cool, steady, alert, a stranger to fear. Over the horrible din he heard the shrill notes of a bugle. Several men in the saloon, ex-soldiers, swore and blanched. "That's the Army call to rally!" Moments later another, different call grated on their ears. "They're going to charge! Who in the devil taught them to fight Army-style?"

Charge the Comanches did, wave after wave, fresh attack on fresh attack for a long, hideous hour. Then they withdrew to the sandhills two hundred yards away and took up a steady sniping.

In the lull the men in Hanrahan's shouted to those in Myers' and Rath's. They counted off names. Not a single white man injured or dead!

Then Dixon swore, the first time Billy had ever heard him do so. "The Shadlers!"

Men bit their lips. It was best not to think of the Shadlers, even though they had never had a chance and couldn't have been rescued. What happened to the Shadlers could have been every man's fate if the cracking ridgepole hadn't awakened them just before the attack.

In the late afternoon the spine-chilling notes rang out again, and the Indians made another charge. By nightfall the ground was littered with dead Indians, horses, oxen, burned wagons, Indian saddles and shields and broken lances. When it was briefly dark before moonrise Billy and Dixon slipped over to Rath's for more ammunition. Others, running bent-kneed and zigzagging, helped. Warriors skulking near enough flung arrows into the shadows. Billy Tyler took one in the lung and died.

Tyler's death rocked Billy, maybe because they were the same age and alike in temperament. For the first time Billy realized, That could have been me. I could have been killed.

He tasted fear momentarily, almost felt Death's cold breath on his face. This wasn't just a skirmish. He and the others were fighting for their lives. They could lose!

He returned to his post at Dixon's side. None fought with more courage or grim purposefulness. Some declared afterward that Billy's eyes turned from blue to cold slate-gray that night. Certainly his boyish lightheartedness and heedlessness were erased by a maturing realization of the value of life itself.

For four more days Death breathed down the neck of every man behind the barricades. In the end it was the long-range Sharps that won the fight for the hunters. The Comanches withdrew to two hundred yards, three, five, seven hundred, a thousand yards, and still lost warriors and horses to the expert marksmen. But before the white men realized they had won, William Olds accidentally shot himself with his own gun and died in his wife's arms. His friends tried in vain to comfort the woman who had stood by them day and night, reloading their guns, making coffee and biscuits.

At sunset the fifth day Billy opened the door at Hanrahan's. The stench inside was unbearable. His face was blackened with powder smoke, streaked with sweat; his eyes were inflamed; his clothing was sticking to his body. "Hanged if I'll be gassed to death!"

"You gone loco!" Hanrahan roared, barring the door again.

"There hasn't been a shot our way since last night," Billy protested.

The men were sure the silence was a trap, that any moment would bring another attack. "We're trapped. We're runnin' out o' ammunition."

"Somebody's got to ride to Dodge for help."

Billy volunteered first, and Dixon second. Under cover of darkness they rode out on the two strongest horses, rode till each was saddle-galled and exhausted. They made it to Dodge and sent forty men to relieve the survivors.

Until this moment, with duty discharged and danger remote, life during the siege had been too grim for Billy to appreciate the drama at Adobe Walls and his part in it. But suddenly he found himself the center of attention. Crowds gathered to hear his story; offered free drinks, food. Dixon disappeared and Billy had the limelight to himself.

He didn't disappoint his admirers. He played the hero to the hilt.

5.   ARMY SCOUT

THE ATTACK ON ADOBE WALLS PROVED TO BE ONLY ONE INCI-
dent in an all-out Indian war that brought bloodshed and
terror from the Arkansas to the Rio Bravo. Hunting buffalo
was out of the question until the Army swept the prairie
clean of the marauders. With each tribe having split into
numerous swift and elusive attacking parties, the Army
faced a formidable task.

Billy was disgusted. He wouldn't go home, as some did,
because he was still broke. He missed Dixon, who had faded
out the moment Billy began bragging up their experiences.
He moseyed around town and located Dixon at the livery
stable. "Where you been all this time?"

"Waiting for you to get tired of grandstanding." Dixon
was saddling a horse.

"Aw shucks, I was only having fun. You going some-
where?"

"To the fort."

"You're not throwin' in with the soldier boys!" Billy
shared a contempt most frontiersmen had for soldiers, in-
tolerantly classifying them as no-good scum.

"Colonel Miles sent for me," Dixon said tersely as he tightened the cinch and adjusted the stirrups.

"You're going to snap to for some barrel-butted windbag of a parade leader?"

Dixon shoved his thumbs in his belt and took a deep breath. "You're in a bad way, Billy. You've been so busy bellied up to Kelley's bar, mooching drinks and throwing it around what a big hero you are that you forgot twenty-eight others fought through that siege and, if they hadn't, you'd be drawn and quartered by now. You're developing into a first-class bull thrower. If that's what you want, stay away from me. Go back to Kelley's, where you belong."

Billy paled as his friend's words flicked the hide off his self-esteem. No other man on earth could have talked to him that way without having his teeth knocked down his throat. But Billy took it from Dixon without protest or whimper because in his heart he knew Dixon was right. Dixon was laying it on the line: go back to Kelley's and the company of bums, or choose the company of men. Although he couldn't have felt worse if he'd been flogged, Billy looked Dixon straight in the eye and said, "I deserved that. But I'll be hanged if I'll thank you for it."

The hunter relaxed, the contempt in his glance softening. "I hate to see a good man turning into a bum." Then he mounted his horse. His lips flicked in a slight smile as he added, "You going to saddle up, or walk to the fort?"

Billy saddled up.

The horses wanted to run, but the riders held them in. It was broiling hot. The grass had dried up; the ground was cracked from drought. By the time they covered the five miles to the fort, both men had to mop their faces and the sweatbands inside their hats. Billy raked his fingers through his mop of black hair and straightened his shirt when an orderly appeared to direct them to the commandant's office.

"Dixon!" the Colonel greeted the hunter, rising from his desk and extending a hand.

Even before he was introduced, Billy realized this man was no barrel-butted windbag of a parade leader. He looked every inch the youngish New Englander who had won his promotions on the battlefield in the Civil War, and had later made the Fifth Infantry one of the crack frontier regiments. The Colonel, in turn, introduced two men who had risen from straight-backed chairs: Lieutenant Frank Baldwin and Ben Clark. Billy knew both by reputation: Baldwin, the only man awarded two Congressional Medals of Honor; Clark, Miles's number-one scout with a record of exploits second to none.

"Sit down, gentlemen," Miles said. Even as he settled his lean flanks on the uncomfortable chair, Billy was humbly grateful that he had chosen the company of men. And what men! He wanted their respect and, by hang, he'd go all-out to deserve it!

The commandant began: "I won't waste time discussing the Indian situation. We all know how bad it is. In a few days Lieutenant Baldwin and Clark are going to lead a column south of the Arkansas. We're going to hit those Indians so hard they'll never dare harass or kill another white man, woman, or child." He pointed to a map behind him. "Our column will hit them on the north. Major Price is moving east from New Mexico, Colonel MacKenzie from Texas, and Colonel Davidson is already marching west out of the Indian Territory. None of us is stopping until we've run those red devils to the ground for good."

Miles looked directly at Dixon. "I asked you here because I know your reputation as an Indian fighter." He eyed Billy speculatively. "I don't know you, Masterson, but the fact that Dixon brought you says a lot." He turned his attention back to the hunter. "I understand you know the country south of here from several seasons' hunting. I hear you've had firsthand contact recently with the Comanches. Now the Army needs two men to assist Baldwin and Clark. I'm sorry to ask you to put yourselves in danger when I can't offer more than the regular scout's wages of thirty dollars a month and rations. I'm assuming that your loyalty to your country puts service above salary."

Serve his country? Billy hadn't thought of it that way. He remembered how mad he had been when he was too young to serve for the Union in the Civil War. You bet he'd like to serve his country. He'd do it for biscuits and bullets, if necessary.

Dixon's eyes, crow-tracked at the corners from years of squinting at the sun, sparkled. "Life out here isn't going to be worth a hoot until the Indians are controlled on reservations. I accept the assignment."

When Miles looked at him, Billy nodded. He had no sympathy for the Indians. If the government offered them reservations and food, they ought to oblige and leave the prairie to the whites.

After a brief discussion of strategy in which, Billy noticed, the military men deferred to Clark and Dixon, Colonel Miles concluded: "One more thing. We received word yesterday that the Cheyennes struck at some ranches along the Smoky Hill River. They murdered a Mr. and Mrs. Germain and their son, and kidnapped the four Germain sisters." Miles consulted a paper. "Catherine, sixteen; Sophy, fourteen; Julia, six; Addie, four. Last report they headed south. I doubt they'll harm the girls because they have high value as hostages." Miles smiled. "It would be a fine thing to rescue them."

Billy walked out on a cloud. Goshallhemlock, what a deal! Serve his country, assist the Army, and rescue helpless maidens. Eeee-yuh! Already he could see himself shooting his way through a hundred bloodthirsty warriors, killing them all and sweeping the tearful, grateful lovelies into his arms! He was all but dancing when he mounted and rode back to Dodge with Dixon. But he was careful to match his outer mood and expression to Dixon's: properly serious. And I'll keep my big mouth shut, he vowed.

Several days later Dixon and Masterson and six Delawares expert in tracking led the way south across the Arkansas to the head of Crooked Creek. Not far behind them rode Lieutenant Baldwin and Ben Clark and the cavalry troop, Clark ranging east and west like a lone panther, and behind them the main column under Colonel Miles.

Spangful of confidence, Billy thought he knew the country; but Dixon and the Delawares showed him a thing or two about slipping through Indian-infested sandhills. Just when Billy had decided there weren't any Indians around, they came onto the smoking, bloodied remains of a surveyors' camp: five men, oxen, and a dog literally torn to pieces.

Dixon pointed to a water barrel riddled with bullet holes. Out of necessity in the past the Cheyennes were stingy with bullets. Now the barrel served as a brazen message: *We are well armed. We have plenty of ammunition.*

While the Delawares buried the dead, Dixon and Billy stood guard, Billy thinking hard. By hang, I'm going to look, and hear, and smell, and feel, and develop whatever that sixth sense of danger is that the best scouts have. I'm going to be as good as Clark and Dixon at this. Adobe Walls, Dixon's brief scorn, the lessons inherent in the surveyors' tragedy tempered Billy's usual irrepressible confidence. I'd better learn, if I want to live.

The Cheyennes led them a crazy chase deeper and deeper into the desolate, sun-parched wilderness. Scarcely a day passed that Baldwin's or Miles's men didn't have a skirmish or two, but the eight scouts out front, through cunning and ability to cover their tracks while still apprising the military, had no trouble. Billy learned to "read the wind," as he called it, sharpening his sense of smell for the slightest alien whiff; seeing puffs of dust, a bent blade of grass as danger signals. He learned to walk noiselessly over the brittle grass, to belly through thickets, to sweat and thirst and hunger as he never had before. He spent many a twenty-four-hour period without uttering more than half a dozen whispered words. Yet he never felt more alive, nor more grateful to be alive. The challenge of survival whetted his capabilities to their highest degree of perfection.

Daytime temperatures soared to a hundred degrees; water holes dried up; mirages confused them; men and horses began dropping. But one day the scouts brought the soddies of Adobe Walls into focus in the field glasses. "No activity down there," Dixon said, handing them to Billy. He saw gun barrels glistening from the slits in the bastions. "We better go in alone."

While the Delawares signaled Baldwin's column to halt, Billy and Dixon rode down to the little fort. As soon as they were recognized, several men ran toward them. It took only a few moments to learn that the rescuers from Dodge had long since departed. The twelve left to guard the supplies had been in a state of almost perpetual siege. Only that morning one of their number had dared venture along the creek to pick wild plums, and was scalped in sight of his companions. But there was water aplenty in the well, and hay and grain in the storehouses. "Bring on the Army!" they urged.

They all gained rest and relief at the settlement. Before pushing south, Colonel Miles dispatched Dixon and three soldiers to carry messages to and from Fort Supply to the east. He had some word that the four-pronged squeeze was working effectively against the Indians and they were on the run, but he wanted to be reasonably sure that he wasn't moving too fast.

Billy was miffed at not being sent with Dixon; but orders

were orders, and he was learning to accept discipline. When the time came to move on, Miles commandeered the remaining supplies at Adobe Walls, and its defenders joined the military. The little fort was now officially abandoned.

The Delawares being strangers to this country, Lieutenant Baldwin sent Billy across the Canadian to scout the burnt badlands ahead. This was more like it! Now he was on his own. Day after day he wormed his way through dry gullies, careful not to raise a puff of smoke or send dirt trickling down steep, eroded banks. The days were still blistering hot, but the nights were getting colder. August days dropped off the calendar.

On August 30, 1874, Miles's column was picking its way across the Staked Plains of Texas, knowing they had the southern Cheyennes on the run now. Small comfort when the chase was through red and yellow canyoned badlands. Billy had gone ahead alone for four hours that morning, and returned to report "not a smell of an Indian sign." But he had learned from Clark that the time to be most careful was when you didn't see any sign at all, and he told Baldwin this.

Baldwin moved his cavalry slowly. They were proceeding along the base of vermilioned cliffs when, without warning, the gullies exploded with yowling, rifled warriors.

Billy grabbed his Army carbine out of the saddle holster, leaped from the saddle, and started firing before he hit the ground. Although the Army gun was lighter than a Sharps, it could be fired faster. As Indians swarmed from the rocks, the well-trained cavalry rallied to Baldwin's shouted commands and began an orderly, blistering attack.

The hills echoed the shooting. Miles heard and came on the double, ordering the Gatling gun to the front. His foot soldiers cut loose while the experimental Gatling machine gun, spouting three hundred shots a minute, raked the cliffs with a deadly rapid fire that terrorized the Indians and

put them to flight. Baldwin ordered his men to mount and
took out across the forbidding country; he didn't stop until
the main body of attackers was dead.

Reunited finally, the Army scoured the Red River country and the Grand Canyon of the Tule, relentlessly searching
out stray bands in the face of a blue norther, a storm fore-
casting the approach of winter. Then Miles ordered Baldwin to contact a supply camp on the Washita River and
bring back food and ammunition. The lieutenant lined up
twenty-three empty wagons, concealed a company of infantry under the canvas tops, and put the cavalry and a light
cannon at the front. Before turning a wheel he sent Billy
ahead to scout.

On the morning of November 8, Billy slipped out alone.
Thin, grim lips swollen from constant sun blisters, the skin
around his eyes creased from constant squinting, hair and
worn trousers and shirt stiff with dust, he moved like a
ghost across the land. A mile from McClellan's Creek he
froze, like a bird dog coming to point. His lips parted; white
teeth showed briefly in his sun-blackened face; then he
streaked to the rear.

"A big Indian village up ahead!" he reported. "Looks like
they're all sleeping. Clark told me they practically hibernate
in the winter."

"Let's wake them up!" Baldwin answered. He turned in
the saddle and roared, "Front into line!" Wagons, cannon
caisson, and cavalry peeled off to form a broad front line.
Baldwin swung his rifle in a forward motion and charged.
Mounted and riding stirrup to stirrup beside him, Billy
started hollering like the Comanches who had poured down
on Adobe Walls. The soldiers took up the cry as they
stormed the Indian village.

The warriors of Gray Beard's camp offered little resistance
and before long the fight was over. While the wounded and
the women and children were being rounded up, Billy rode

through the camp, ferreting out lurking snipers. He noticed
a large buffalo robe on the ground; it was humped in the
middle, moving crabwise over the grass. He dismounted
and ran light-footed to it, rifle readied on his right arm,
fingers curled for firing. With his left hand he yanked the
robe aside. Two dirty, starved, ragged little girls screeched
in terror.

Billy gasped and began to back off. Then he saw the girls
were blue-eyed, saw white skin through their rags. He
dropped to one knee. "Julia? Addie?"

Addie cried, but Julia's eyes widened. He talked softly,
"Julia, don't be afraid. See, I'm a white man." He pulled
his shirt sleeve back to the elbow so they could see. "The
soldiers came to rescue you from the bad Indians. That's
what the shooting was about." He inched closer and held
out one hand. "Don't be afraid."

When both girls clung to each other, he put down the
rifle and gathered a child in each arm; pressed his cheek
against their hair; talked softly, crooningly to them. "Everything is going to be all right," he kept saying over and over.
Then he started walking through the ravaged camp, his
strong arms comforting the little hostages. Julia put one
clawlike hand out and touched his ragged whiskers. "Papa
had whiskers. Indians don't." Then she curved her arm
around his neck and hugged him fiercely.

"Heaven help us! What have you got there, Masterson,
an armful of rags?" Lieutenant Baldwin rode up to Billy.
Other soldiers gathered around quickly.

"I found two of the Germain sisters, sir; Julia and Addie."

"Hooray!" Baldwin tossed military decorum and his hat
to the winds. The soldiers cheered too, but it frightened the
girls so that they quieted. When the lieutenant tried to
speak, he found himself choking up. What could he say to
the unshaven, wild-looking scout who had tears of joy
running down his gunsmoke-blackened cheeks?

By March 1, 1875, Colonel Miles's men had subdued the remaining Cheyennes. Chief Stone Calf had surrendered Catherine and Sophy, the two older Germain sisters. The entire company was called to attention; foot soldiers, cavalrymen, and civilian scouts lined up face to face across a twenty-foot strip. From a wagon nearby, Scout Masterson lifted Julia to the ground. She clung to his hand as he carried Addie to the long line of troopers. "Now watch," he told them, "you're going to have a b-i-g surprise."

In a few moments two slender, shy, bewildered young women were escorted down the line of soldiers toward Billy. When they saw their two small sisters they screamed and ran forward. Then everyone was cheering and throwing their hats again.

As Billy turned Julia and Addie over to Catherine and Sophy, he wiped his nose and exclaimed, "Holy smackers, the campaign was worth it—every bloody mile of it! Hip, hip, hooray for the Germain sisters!"

6. BAT

THE NEXT DAY COLONEL MILES SUMMONED BILLY TO HIS headquarters. "Masterson, to show my appreciation of your valuable service in a difficult campaign, I am assigning you to the inactive scouting force at Fort Elliott, Texas, near here. You deserve a rest. I assure you that, unless we run into another hot spot of Indian trouble, your duties will consist largely in drawing your pay. By fall we should have the Indians thoroughly subdued, and you can decide then whether you want to continue with the Army or not."

Billy thought fast. He was broke, and a long way from a job or home. If he returned to hunting buffalo—and he had doubts about that—it would not be until fall. "Thank you, sir. I accept the assignment."

Within a few days Billy threw his small sack of belongings under a cot in the barracks of Fort Elliott. Learning the town of Sweetwater was nearby, he spruced up in clean Army-issue cottons and rode in for a look. Although he missed Dixon, still out on another mission, he had never been at a loss in making friends. "Gosh, it's been so long

since I set foot in a town, I'll probably stampede at the
sight of the town pump."

At first glance Sweetwater didn't offer much more than
the usual dusty wide main street flanked by false-fronted
buildings, the wooden awnings casting sharp shadows
across the planked walks. For a moment Billy yearned for
the dry Kansas air rather than the muggy furnace blast
that fried a man's skin. He thought of the thirty dollars
just received from the Army paymaster. Not enough for a
whim-wham of a spree, but anything would be better than
moping around the fort. His finger tips itched. It was a
long time since he had tried his hand at faro or poker.

He dismounted, wrapped the reins around a hitching rail,
and stepped into the Lady Gay dance hall. One whiff of
tobacco smoke; one glance at the fairly large dance floor
ringed with tables, the bar crowded with men, the air buzz-
ing pleasantly with male talk and a tinkling piano, and he
took the first happy relaxed breath in months. Thank
heavens for the Lady Gay type of amusement places in the
frontier towns, the only ones where men could meet and
be companionable over a glass or card game. By frontier
standards these were considered respectable, were well
policed. They served good food and were favorite hangouts
for the better class of men.

Billy began circulating about the room. A smile on his
lips, he nodded right and left, tapped his fingers in time
to the music. All the chairs were occupied at the poker
tables, but a faro dealer sat idly riffling cards on a felt-
topped table. Was luck with him? Billy wondered. If so,
he just might run that thirty dollars up to a tidy sum.

"Deal 'em out," he said to the rather foppish-looking,
dark-haired dealer whose mustache was waxed in stiff
points. The man snubbed out a cigar and opened the game.
In faro the player bets against the dealer as to which cards
turn up. When Billy won three games in a row, a few men

gathered to watch. He played on, losing now and then, but winning enough so that after several hours he had two hundred dollars. In that time he and the dealer had exchanged no pleasantries, only the words necessary to carry on the game.

"Hate to break a winning streak, but I need to take on a steak. Care to join me?" Billy asked him.

"Some other time."

Billy pocketed his winnings and moved to the counter where food was served. "Biggest steak in the house," he ordered.

The chow tender slapped a mug of coffee in front of him, and volunteered the information that the faro dealer was none other than Ben Thompson, notorious Texas bad man and killer.

A likely story, Billy thought. All Texans were supposed to be tough hombres.

"That's a fact," the hasher insisted. "You ain't been around long if you don't know Ben. He's got a brother, Billy, who's even worse."

Billy resumed playing cards with Ben.

About two in the morning Ben called it quits.

"Drinks on me." Billy ordered coffee; Ben, a quart of brandy. "Talk to me," he said quietly.

Because his sense of humor had let him see himself as braggy and ridiculous, as he really was the time he made Ritter pay off, Billy told the story amusingly. Soon Thompson was chuckling. Meanwhile Billy was studying the gambler-killer. For all his foppish looks, he appeared to be a man haunted by ghosts. Must be, if he needs a quart of liquor for a nightcap, Billy decided, and spun another story. Others listened from tables nearby, but none joined the twosome. So, Billy decided, Thompson was also a lonely man.

Everyone within hearing soon knew about the siege of

Adobe Walls and the rescue of the Germain sisters. When Billy returned to the Lady Gay after sleeping all day through, he discovered he was a hero again. Inside of a week he was on a first-name basis with the regulars at the Lady Gay. He shed the terse modesty patterned after Dixon. He wisecracked, laughed, and freely spent his winnings. He thrived on late hours, suspenseful card games, and the smoky atmosphere.

He learned that, like most tough hombres, Ben Thompson had had his comeuppance. He had tried to shoot up Ellsworth, Kansas, and hold the town at bay with his guns. The Mayor tried to make his Marshal and deputies disarm Thompson, but they turned in their badges. Then a slim young fellow of twenty-six pinned on a badge, walked smack out across the open plaza, and talked Thompson into not only holstering his guns but paying a fine for disturbing the peace. The story of Ben's being backed into a hole spread like wildfire. "But don't you rib him," Billy was warned. "He's trigger-touchy about it."

Billy was puzzled. "I still can't figure why Ben didn't shoot that new Marshal fellow."

"He said afterward he couldn't shoot a young feller with that much guts. But he 'lows next time he meets Wyatt Earp there won't be no time for talk."

Wyatt Earp! Billy's eyes lighted up. He had lost track of Earp. Remembering the man's incredibly swift draw and marksmanship, he thought Ben Thompson had been smart not to draw against him.

The weeks slipped by much to Billy's liking. He reported now and then to Fort Elliott but spent most of his time in Sweetwater. So far he had resisted invitations from the dance-hall girls at the Lady Gay to cut a caper on the dance floor. Not that he didn't like girls. He just didn't know what to think of these. He had been raised to believe that there were two kinds of women: good, like his mother

and sisters, and bad, like the hard-faced women who frequented the low dives in Dodge City.

But these girls at the Lady Gay were different. Most were
halfway pretty, conducted themselves nicely for all their
laughing and dancing, wore attractive clean cotton dresses,
and were treated with respect. The cowboys and soldiers
were sparking some, and made no bones about wanting to
marry them.

One evening when a pert black-haired girl with white
skin as yet untouched by the Texas sun smiled at him and
asked if he would dance, Billy found himself nodding, and
smiling into her blue eyes. Noticing that Billy was attracted
to the girl, Ben Thompson introduced them. "This is Molly
Brennan, Billy. She's brand-new here." He turned his thumb
toward Billy. "And this here is the handsomest dog in
Texas."

Billy's eyes flashed. He was glad of the heeled boots that
gave him more height. He followed Molly to the dance floor
and put an arm around her slim waist. "I haven't danced
for so long I'll probably tromp all over you."

But he didn't. When the bouncy fiddle and piano music
began, he kicked up his heels like a young horse. Molly was
thistledown in his arms. Her laughter was soft and ladylike.

"Buy a drink?" Molly asked, as she was supposed to.

For a moment Billy hesitated. For some reason the
thought of this pretty, seemingly nice girl having a drink
rankled. But he knew the girls at the Lady Gay made their
living on commissions earned on dance tickets and the
drinks their partners bought. "Sure thing," he agreed, and
was soon carrying two glasses to a table. When they were
seated, he noticed Molly's drink was a slightly different
color from his. "What's that you're drinking?"

"Oh, my special brand," she said, her cheeks flushing.

On impulse Billy raised her glass to his lips. "Tea!"

"Shhhh!" Molly implored. "Do you want to get me fired?

Of course it's tea. That's all we girls ever drink. The boss would be furious if he knew you found out you paid for whisky for me, and I ended up with tea."

"Your secret is safe with me," Billy assured her, much relieved. "Say, I enjoyed that dance. Ben mentioned you were new here. Where you from?"

Molly laughed. "I didn't say."

Billy's eyes lingered on the dark ringlets, blue eyes, and red lips. Most of the white women he had seen since coming West were wind-parched and prematurely aged; Molly reminded him of a flower-scented breeze.

The girl dimpled at him. "So you're Billy Masterson. Someone pointed you out to me when you came in tonight. I had heard about the siege of Adobe Walls back in . . ." She hesitated, then chattered on, "And I heard about your rescuing those two little Germain sisters. My goodness, a man who did all those brave things should be at least a hundred years old!"

Billy's heart thumped, but his eyes sparkled with devilment as he joked, "I'm really as old as Methuselah, but the weather's so durn hot I had to clip my beard. I was getting heat rash on my knees!"

The two laughed and danced and talked for an hour, happy in each other's company.

Meantime a number of soldiers of the Fourth Cavalry stationed at Fort Elliott swaggered into the Lady Gay. They elbowed the cowboys away from the girls. One, a Sergeant King, insisted on dancing with Molly. Billy took offense at the soldier's officious manner; but Molly intervened quickly, saying, "See you tomorrow night."

She was asking him not to make trouble for her. Billy joined Thompson. "Who is that loudmouth dancing with Molly?"

Thompson sneered. "A fatheaded brawler and troublemaker. Likes to pick fights and shoot up the place. Gets away with it down here, but not up north."

Billy scented a story. "What happened up north?"

"If King knew the news had leaked down here, he'd blow his top. Seems like he takes leave every spring and rides trail north to Kansas. He's buddy-buddy with the cowboys; that's why they let him push them around here. Well, him and his loudmouthed friends blew into Wichita a few months ago and started hurrahing the town. But Wichita's got a new Marshal backing up an ordinance that says it's against the law to wear guns inside the city limits. Our bully-boy here decided he'll just tree that Marshal. He sees the fellow on the street, pulls both guns on him, and dares the Marshal to take them off him." Ben stopped long enough to guffaw. "What a jolt King got! This Marshal walks right up to King, yanks his guns off him, slaps his face; then grabs him by the neck and kites him all the way to the jail, and fines him a hunnerd dollars." Then Ben added grimly, "King should have knowed better than try to tree Wyatt Earp."

Earp again! Billy sucked in his cheeks so as not to grin. "You know Earp?" he asked with feigned innocence.

Thompson flicked him a gray-eyed glance so murderous that Billy felt as if he had just swallowed a pitcher of ice water. But he kept his look so bland and steady that Thompson guessed Billy didn't know about his run-in with Earp, or he wouldn't have dared asked the question that could have precipitated a shooting. But on second thought, Ben figured swiftly, Billy was sure to have heard the story. His admiration for Billy tripled. The youngster had guts! "I know Earp," he snapped. "You ever run across his trail?"

"He taught me how to use a six-gun," Billy answered quietly.

Only by a twitch of the eyelids could Billy tell that

Thompson digested this bit of information. "Don't ever prod me into a gunfight with you, Billy," he warned.

"Long as we're on the same side of the fence, I won't."

The gambler gave Billy a long, hard look. In a round-about way the youngster was saying that as long as Thompson behaved within the limits of the law, they would remain friends. But Masterson was also inferring that he was not afraid of the older man.

Billy returned to watching Molly and the sergeant. King was monopolizing her time; obviously pouring sweet talk in her pretty ears.

Seeing the annoyed look on his face, Ben asked, "Want me to toss him out?"

"I'll take care of him if he steps on my toes. Besides, it would only make trouble for Molly." He even kept his temper when he heard King bragging later, after Molly was dancing with others, that "when I sweet-talk 'em, they swoon like flies." His friends assured him he was the smoothest lady-killer in all of Texas.

For many evenings Billy danced with Molly and played cards while she danced with others, including the obnoxious King.

Ben tried to twit him about the girl. "Ain't you jealous?"

"Nope," Billy answered good-naturedly.

"Wouldn't blame you for falling in love with her. She's a nice little thing."

"Whoa there. Slow down, Ben. I'm not falling in love. Molly is lots of fun, but it doesn't go any farther than that."

"She's crazy about you."

"Love 'em and leave 'em, that's my motto," Billy lied to cover up the fact that Molly was the first girl he had ever paid any attention. But that still didn't alter the fact that his feelings for her were not serious. He cherished his freedom; he didn't plan to stay long in Texas. Maybe under different circumstances . . . if he'd met her at a church social . . . if he hadn't been raised so strictly . . . that streak of fastidiousness ingrained in him, that made him avoid profanity and gutter talk, that made him be clean physically and morally, maybe that's what kept him from falling head over heels for Molly.

He continued to frequent the Lady Gay, dance with Molly, and play cards. He ignored King, who tried a little harder each evening to prod Billy into a fight.

The regulars began laying quiet bets with one another on how long it would be before a real fight broke out. Then they bet on which man would win.

A few nights later King and his bunch of rowdies, well fortified with liquor, roared into town and all but split their horses' mouths reining up in front of the Lady Gay. King elbowed through the doors and stood, hands on hips, surveying the crowd. His face purpled. His girl was dancing with that fresh-faced Masterson pup! He strode toward the dance floor, knocking men out of his way like tenpins.

He grabbed Billy's arm. "Molly's my girl. The next time I catch you dancing with her I'll blow the living daylights out o' you!"

Billy's slate-gray eyes narrowed. "Take your hand off me, King."

Dancers retreated from the trouble spot. Someone waved to the piano player and he paused in mid-note.

"Why, you—" King grabbed for his gun.

Molly darted a hand to his wrist and stepped in front of him so he could not unholster his gun fully. "Stop it! Do you want me to lose my job? If you make trouble for me, I'll never dance another step with you." Although deathly pale, she forced herself to smile. "My goodness, I can't have the customers drawing guns over me." She turned frantic eyes toward Billy. "You won't mind if I dance with the sergeant?"

"As you say, Molly. But don't ever again step between

two men having an argument. You could be killed." He smiled thinly at King. "Next time be sober, Sergeant, I'd like to give you at least a sporting chance."

The piano player tore into a schottische. Molly put her arms up to King before he could carry on the fight. Dancers and card players jerked into motion. The tension shattered in laughter and music.

Though the immediate danger was over, King returned to the fort in a foul mood. He had liquor hidden in his locker and started drinking. The more he drank, the more he was convinced that Masterson had stolen his girl and insulted him. By the next evening he was spoiling for revenge. Once more he raced into Sweetwater with the usual pack of no-goods at his heels.

Billy was dancing with Molly. Disregarding those in his way, King started firing his revolver. At the first shot Billy whirled around, saw who it was, and grabbed for his six-gun. With his left arm he swung Molly away from him. But the moment she spotted King's gun, she screamed and threw herself in front of Billy. She caught the full impact of King's bullet and reeled backwards against Billy's right arm. He couldn't fire. Another shot from King shattered Billy's hip. He lurched momentarily, caught Molly with his left arm, and with one shot drilled King through the heart.

As Billy crumpled to the floor, King's comrades rushed to finish him. But Ben Thompson leaped up on the faro table, six-gun in each hand, and stopped them cold. He made them back up, submit to being disarmed and booted out of the hall.

Ben holstered his guns; jumped to the floor and ran to Billy, who was unconscious. Molly was dead.

"You light out to the fort and tell Colonel Miles what happened to Billy," Ben ordered two men. "Tell Miles I want that post surgeon in here pronto; and if he don't come, I'll come after him."

By the time the surgeon arrived, Ben had Billy moved to a table. When it was time to probe for the bullet and mend the hip, Billy began to regain consciousness. Rather than see him suffer, Ben turned Billy's head gently and tapped him hard behind the ear. Billy passed out and missed the excruciating operation.

For weeks he was out of commission. The bullet had smashed some small bones and the wound was a long time healing. Much as he hated it, Billy walked with a limp and began using a cane.

No longer fit for scouting, he asked to be released from further duty with the Army. Ben had provided for his care during his convalescence; and he got the proprietor of the Lady Gay to hire Billy to keep order in the place, when he was up and about.

Billy accepted the job. It wasn't hard work and he wanted more time to recuperate before returning North. A good many had witnessed the fight and commented on his fast, deadly shot under almost impossible circumstances.

"Masterson's no one to tangle with," the men told it around.

"He's a killer," they said.

The frontier code judged Billy blameless in the killing of King. He had been fighting in defense of himself and a pretty girl.

He never had to draw his gun again in the Lady Gay. Not that trouble didn't erupt, but Billy discovered that batting the troublemakers on the forehead or behind the ear with the knob of his cane was very effective.

It didn't take him long to acquire a new name that stuck with him the rest of his life.

From now on he was *Bat* Masterson.

7.

DEPUTY UNDER WYATT EARP

LATE IN MAY, 1876, BAT MASTERSON RODE INTO DODGE CITY, dusty, his hip throbbing from hours in the saddle. Otherwise he was full of pepper, his gripsack bulging with fine clothes and his money belt fattened with card winnings.

In the two years that he had been away, Dodge had changed radically. Bat's first inkling was seeing large herds of cattle cropping the grass for a five-mile radius from the railroad town, and numerous tent and blanket camps nearer the city limits. As he rode across the Arkansas River bridge toward Second Avenue he saw pens along the railroad jammed with cattle, and strings of cars on the sidings. Even if this were not evidence enough, he had only to breathe to know cattle had taken over the Queen City of the buffalo hunters.

"What's going on here?" he asked Deacon Cox when he sought a room in Cox's boardinghouse—a private room this time; not a bunk, wall hook, and sack in the common room where he had stayed before.

"We're a cattle capital now." The proprietor explained that, with hundreds of thousands of Texas cattle being driven north to market, the grass along the Chisholm and other trails had given out. As soon as the military quashed the Indian uprising, the Texans started swinging farther west. Dodge supplanted Wichita as the big shipping point.

"It was worth your life to walk on Front Street last summer," Cox continued. "Those Texas cowboys never quit cuttin' up. Bet they fired a million bullets into lamps, windows, mirrors . . . it was fierce! They rode their horses into every place in town. Then they started fightin' the Civil War all over again with every man-jack who fought for the Union. There's over eighty men buried on Boot Hill!"

Bat was fascinated. He had worried about returning to a town that might have all but dried up and blown away since the buffalo hunting had petered out. But if the Texans had taken over the town, life could be very interesting. Sweetwater had taught him that Texans were duds at playing cards. He was tired of their bragging and chicory-thick drawl, but he had a hunch that the pickings would be easy in Dodge for a heads-up gambler like himself.

He started for the stairs leading to his room, then paused. "Didn't anybody try to screw the lid on here last summer?"

"Sure," Cox said. "The city council passed a lot of tomfool ordinances prohibiting carrying or shooting guns inside the city limits and riding horses onto sidewalks or stores, but the merchants howled them down. They figured if the cowboys couldn't have their fun in Dodge, they'd take their business somewheres else. Considerin' they spent over a million dollars in this burg in a few weeks, the merchants wouldn't stand for putting any kind of damper on that. So, next, the council hired Billy Brooks to keep the peace. You remember the old coot?"

Billy nodded. Brooks had been a topnotch hunter.

"Well, Brooks had no more feelings about killing a man than a buffalo. He shot down so many in cold blood that

the cowboys ganged up and shot him out of town. Same
with half a dozen others. And it's startin' all over again.
Only three weeks ago they got rid of Jack Allen, and the
season ain't half under way yet!"

"Dodge is without a lawman?"

"Not by a darn sight! Some former Wichita cattlemen
presently headquartering at Dodge told the new Mayor,
George Hoover, about a lawman who had ringtailed the
Texans at Wichita. Hoover wrote him to come to Dodge
and, by gar, he accepted. Tall fellow . . . kind of a lone
wolf. Got a funny name. Earp, Wyatt Earp."

Bat took the steps three at a time. He couldn't wait to see
Earp!

A little while later Wyatt Earp, wearing black trousers
and vest and a white shirt with black string tie, paused on
Front Street to pass the time of day with Mayor Hoover.

"Heard you had to buffalo some of the boys last night,"
the Mayor commented.

Earp nodded. "Better some soreheads this morning than
fresh buryings on the hill."

"You got enough deputies to back you up? This town will
be howling in another week or so."

"If I can find a good man, I'll put on one more." Earp
glanced up and down the wide rutted street fronting the
north side of the Atchison, Topeka and Santa Fe Railroad
tracks. Over a hundred freight wagons jammed the road,
each drawn by ten, twelve, even sixteen horses or oxen. It
was impossible for horsemen to pass. Cattle owners, their
trail bosses and cowboys, mule skinners, bullwhackers, railroad laborers, and soldiers from the fort tramped the boardwalk or lounged against the newly painted store fronts. The
batwing doors to the gambling houses swung endlessly. On
the south side of the tracks the riffraff and criminal element
kept raucous company with their own kind. The Marshal

wasn't expected to interfere there in anything less than wholesale slaughter.

In spite of the crowd and dust Earp's attention was drawn to a colorfully dressed fellow. "Get a load of that one-man circus parade," he nudged Hoover. A large gray sombrero was cocked too far over one eye for Earp to recognize the dandy; but he had little difficulty in noting the red silk neckerchief knotted under one ear, the light embroidered vest and trousers, wide bright red satin sash tied at the waist, silver-studded belt and holsters sprouting silver-plated ivory-handled revolvers, and the fancily stitched high-heeled boots.

Hoover chuckled. "Walks like he owned the town. Got a gimp in his getalong, though. Must be his spurs are dragging." Gold-mounted spurs and a gold-knobbed cane completed the costume.

When the fellow was only twenty paces from him, Earp's eyebrows shot up under his soft-brimmed hat. "Masterson!"

Bat heard his name, and all but leaped to shake hands. "Earp! Glad to see you. Heard you were in town. How's everything with you?"

"Fine," Earp answered, and coughed to cover the laughter he couldn't hold back. "Sorry . . . The dust . . ." He wiped his eyes. "You spieling for a circus, Billy?"

"What makes you say that? No, I'm on the loose. And it's Bat now, not Billy any more." He tapped his hat jauntily with the knob of his cane. "Got the name batting trouble-makers down in Sweetwater, Texas."

"This was after you rescued the Germain sisters?"

Bat laughed. "You heard about that, eh?" He was pleased. He had written a glowing account to his family. Far from a dutiful chore, he enjoyed the writing and congratulated himself on his flair for words. Otherwise he had left it to several hundred soldiers to garnish the tale and spread it in six directions. Could he help it if he was a hero? Personally, he thought he wore his laurels rather well. He didn't brag or talk himself spitless any more, but of course he didn't have to. Others did it for him.

"You know Mayor Hoover?" Earp asked.

"Congratulations on your new post, Mayor. Have a cigar?" Bat handed Hoover and Earp long, slim, expensive cigars and lit one for himself. A big gold ring in the shape of a snakehead with ruby eyes flashed in the sun as Bat tapped the ashes with his little finger.

Hoover excused himself. Bat and Earp drifted along the boardwalk. For all his jauntiness Bat watched the cold-lidded appraising looks, the arrested talk that marked Earp's passing. He hoped Earp had topnotch men for deputies; sure looked like he was going to need them.

Apparently the Marshal was enforcing the no-guns ordinance. Bat didn't see anyone sporting a firearm other than the lawman himself. Hmmmm . . . that posed a problem. Bat had put a lot of money in his fancy guns. He would hate to rack them, and he'd feel plumb naked without them.

Earp continued on to his office adjoining the new city lockup, a vast improvement on the fifteen-foot hole in the ground formerly used for confining troublemakers. "Want you to meet my deputies," the Marshal said as they went in the door.

Bat took one look at the slim young man seated before a roll-top desk cleaning a rifle. "Jim!"

Jim Masterson's jaw dropped. Then he whooped and embraced his brother.

Bat had known through letters that Ed and Jim had cut their wisdom teeth in Wichita's gamblinghouses and could handle themselves well. "But I never guessed we'd meet out here!" He was jubilant and started to cut a caper, but his spurs bit the rough flooring and almost tripped him. "This calls for a celebration."

"It will have to keep. I'm on duty," Jim answered.

Earp nodded toward his other deputy, Joe Mason, a lanky mustachioed fellow. "Take a couple of hours. We'll keep the lid on the town until you get back." Then he added smoothly, "You can leave those fancy guns with me, Bat."

Bat shrugged. No use making an issue of it, not when Jim was a deputy. He handed over the handsome belt.

The two brothers, Bat twenty-two, Jim twenty—the same height but Jim more subdued in coloring and nature, and drably attired compared to Bat—walked out with their arms on each other's shoulders. When they came abreast of the Long Branch, Jim said, "Best food in town here."

"Better than Dog Kelley's?"

"No, but it's cheaper."

Bat waved his hand grandly. "Only the best for us." They moved down the street a few doors and entered Kelley's. For Bat it was something of a triumphal entry. Kelley and the bartenders greeted their old friend. The hero had to submit to a lot of back-slapping before he and Jim made it to a quiet corner.

While they waited for steaks, Jim reported that their parents and sisters were well. "Pa has a hired man now. Tommy and the girls go to school most all day eight months of the year now."

"I sure wish Ed would come out here," Bat said.

"He's doing pretty good in Wichita. He sells cattle on commission, and crops, and dickers in real estate . . . when he isn't winning at cards." Jim laughed. "After you left home, I was the one Ma kept telling, 'You watch out for Ed. Don't you let nothing bad happen to Ed.' Guess she never will get the idea Ed can look after himself."

"Amen to that! Now tell me about Earp. What is he really like?"

After the steaks, fried potatoes, and peppersass had been served, and the aproned waiter was out of hearing, Jim said between bites, "He's a loner . . . but I got a hunch he's

lonesome. They say he's killed twenty men." Jim whispered,
"Confidentially, he told me he's only killed one so far—a
case of outdraw a man or go under himself. He doesn't mind
the stories . . . says having a reputation for killing keeps
a lot of guys off his neck."

Bat covered his meat with salt and pepper. "He's right."

"Earp's too serious, though," Jim continued. "Hardly ever
smiles. Talks so little you'd think words cost him a nickel
apiece. Even in Wichita he never cut loose and had what
you'd call fun. Played poker like a stone man. Took his
whisky neat but dang little of it." With all the wisdom of
twenty years Jim added, "It's not good for a fellow to be
grim *all* the time. And, Billy, he—"

"It's Bat now."

"And, Bat, every cockroach in Dodge is laying for Earp.
I hear the Texans have put up a thousand-dollar bounty
to anyone who runs him out of town!"

Bat polished off his meal, saying little but thinking hard.
So Earp needed livening up, did he? Well, Bat Masterson
could handle that. But how to help his friend against the
bounty seekers when his only weapon was the cane? That
would take some figuring. 'Course it could be all talk, too.

Then a practical thought hit him. "You pretty fast with a
gun?"

Jim allowed modestly he wasn't exactly a beginner.

Anxious to see whether Jim could really shoot fast enough
to be an effective deputy, Bat challenged, "Match you
shots."

The two returned to the jail. "Want to match shots with
me and Jim?"

Earp nodded. After Bat buckled up, the three walked to
the bridge and crossed it. Even the Marshal had to go outside the city limits for target practice. Using driftwood and
tree stumps as targets, they began blasting away. After a

bit Jim glanced behind them. "We got a crowd watching us."

"Good!" Bat exclaimed. "Let's give 'em something to think about. Twenty says you can't outdraw me and hit that tin can three times in a row!"

Jim almost matched Bat, but Earp outdrew and outshot them both by a quarter-second. The spectators withdrew, some scratching their chins thoughtfully.

Back at the jail, while the three filled the empty loops in their cartridge belts, Earp stated, "Like to have you be my deputy, Bat."

"Well, thanks, friend. I'd like to, but I'm still too stove up for deputying."

"Gimpy leg or not, you're the man I want." The pay was seventy-five dollars a month plus a four-way cut on some eight hundred dollars monthly in bounties earned from the two dollars and a half the council paid Earp for each arrest.

"Dead ones don't count," Earp warned. The idea was to let the boys cut up within limits north of the tracks, but buffalo enough of those who asked for trouble so the word would circulate that hurrahing the respectable side of town and popping off with a gun would result in a very sore head for the offender, not to mention the humiliation. Those who frequented the dives south of the tracks could fight among themselves as long as they didn't cross the tracks, which Earp had earmarked as the Deadline. "Leave that district to me," Earp concluded.

The pay was peanuts compared to what he could earn gambling, but Bat didn't give it a second thought. He had helped the Army for thirty dollars and beans. He'd back up Earp for the same if he had to. It would be interesting, teaching feisty Texans that law and order in western Kansas meant *law* and *order*. "Swear me in."

When he started out to make the rounds with Earp, his

spurs almost tripped him again. He yanked them off and tossed them in a corner. "Send those dang things to Tommy," he told Jim.

Within forty-eight hours numerous cowboys were sprouting lumps on their foreheads, compliments of *Bat* Masterson. To add insult to injury, Bat not only whacked the troublemakers before they could draw, and then disarmed them, but often hauled them outside and turned them headfirst into any one of the many barrels filled with water and set along Front Street for fire protection.

However, hauling one culprit to court provided some unexpected exercise for the new deputy.

At the appointed time Bat escorted a James Martin from the lockup to the courtroom. Martin was plenty soreheaded, not only because he felt unjustly accused of being a horse thief but because of the egg-sized lump on the side of his head, courtesy of Deputy Marshal Masterson.

Judge Joe Frost, presiding over the Dodge City Police Court, happened to be unduly soreheaded also, thanks to a hangover. He flumped down in his chair, banged the gavel, and roared, "The Marshal will preserve strict order! Any person caught throwing turnips, cigar stumps, beets, or old quids of chewing tobacco at this court will be immediately arraigned before the bar of justice." He glared at Martin, banged the gavel once more, and ordered, "Trot out the wicked and unfortunate, and let the cotillion commence."

Sucking in his cheeks to keep from laughing, Bat stepped forward with his prisoner.

"You're arraigned for horse stealing!" the Judge informed Martin.

"That's a lie! Nobody is goin' to fine me for somethin' I ain't done! I'll clear out this whole dang courtroom!"

With that Martin leaped at the Judge and began pummeling him. Bat jumped on his back, but found he was tackling a wild man. The City Attorney piled into the fight, and the

four fought over the bench, upset a table, and sent chairs
tumbling. Bystanders watched, cackling, applauding, and
offering no help. Martin socked the Attorney and sent him
sprawling and dazed into a corner. Then he piled into the
Judge, knocked him over the railing, and bit his thumb
before Frost caved in. Bat pulled him off the Judge and
clobbered him over the ear with a six-gun. Martin merely
shook his head, and turned his flailing fists on Bat. The
two grunted and scuffled, broke two windows before Bat
finally subdued Martin with a determined fist to the
prisoner's jaw.

Highly amused at seeing his attorney sagging in one
corner and the deputy marshal's fancy suit split, torn, and
bloodied, Judge Frost regained his chair. He licked his
bleeding thumb, and once more banged the gavel. Then
he leaned forward and addressed the gasping Martin, "Why,
instead of allowing the demon of passion to fever your brain
into this fray, did you not shake hands and call it a mistake?
But no! You went to chawing and clawing and pulling hair.
Ten dollars and costs, Mr. Martin!"

Martin paid the fine.

"Court dismissed!" the Judge declared, although there
were others to be arraigned. "Now, boys," he addressed
the Attorney, Martin, and Masterson, "why don't we all go
to Kelley's and I'll stand for a round of drinks!"

As Bat was to write many, many years later, in describing
the life of Dodge City during the cattle-trail days, "Justice
was dispensed informally. Courtroom procedures bore small
resemblance to those of more civilized communities."

As June temperatures rose, Bat discarded the Mexican
sash and the embroidered vest, and finally swapped the
cumbersome sombrero for a soft-brimmed black hat like
Earp's. But he kept the high-heeled boots. Without them
he was shorter than Jim, and that he could not tolerate.

One very hot day he held Earp's guns while the Marshal

accepted the town bully's invitation to put up his fists. Earp let the cowboy start swinging before he broke his jaw. He wasn't even breathing hard when he buckled on his gun belt.

Another night while Bat was patrolling Front Street a man came on the run across the tracks to say Earp was holding off forty cowboys, his back up against the wall of a dance hall on the south side. No matter that running was painful, Bat took off across the Deadline.

"Keep this gang under control while I take on this big-mouthed fellow who says he can put a head on me," Earp ordered with icy calm.

One look at the challenger and Bat advised, "Don't do it. It's a trap. Your boy is one of the toughest scrappers in all of Texas. I saw him beat a man to death at Sweetwater."

It took Earp thirty minutes to finish the fight. Bat wrote Ed later, "Wyatt carried the fight to that big bruiser every second. He had the fellow whipped in the first five minutes, but couldn't finish him immediately. Wyatt ended with his shirt and undershirt torn off, badly bruised and plastered with bloody mud. But that fight had a lot to do with the rest of the summer being pretty tame."

Trouble slacked off to the point where Deputy Marshal Masterson began to get bored. When he heard that a pompous big-time politician from the East was stopping overnight at Dodge, he planned an elaborate joke. He rounded up his cronies and suggested they don Indian bonnets and other regalia displayed in the various places about town, and then gather east of town. Meantime with Earp and Mayor Hoover he welcomed the bigwig off the train and talked him into going antelope hunting not five miles from Dodge.

"Nice chance to get a trophy head for your office, Congressman," Earp said, as straight-faced as ever, though he was in on the prank.

Mayor Hoover assured the visitor, "Don't worry about your marksmanship. You'll get your trophy one way or another."

The Congressman didn't know an antelope from an elk, but was impressed with Dodge hospitality. Displaying a trophy head back East might be nice publicity. "You boys will be hunting with me?"

"Yes indeed," they chorused enthusiastically.

On the way, Earp regaled the guest with trumped-up accounts of Indian massacres that supposedly took place in this or that draw they were passing. As the select party was rounding a grove of cottonwoods, a band of painted, howling savages exploded out of the shadows.

Earp shouted, "Ride for your life! We'll fight 'em off!"

The unsuspecting greenhorn wheeled his horse, slammed his pointed shoes into its sides, and rode pell-mell for town. Earp and Masterson and Hoover fired their guns in the air and the "Indians" put on a convincing attack. The Congressman yanked up before the Long Branch in Dodge, flung himself to the ground, and staggered into the gambling-house yelling, "Indian attack! To arms!"

When the room rocked with hoots and guffaws, the enraged man stomped to the station and demanded that a special train take him to Wichita at once. But when he saw the pranksters return, all but prostrate from laughing, he decided to play the good sport rather than become more of a laughingstock. After a gusty celebration he fatuously accepted the gift of an antelope head, unaware that rabbit ears had been substituted on the trophy.

Dodge thought well of a marshal who joined in playing this practical joke, as well as others engineered in Bat's fertile brain. But soon even these jokes became tiresome. When word reached Dodge of a gold strike in the Black Hills of South Dakota, Bat suggested to Jim and Wyatt, "Let's go!"

Earp shook his head. "Gave my word to the Mayor I'd stay here until September."

"I hate like heck leaving you shorthanded," Bat told him.

"You won't," Earp assured him. "My brother Morgan is arriving this week. He'll take your place."

With that, Bat readily resigned his commission. "How about you, Jim?"

His younger brother chose to remain with Wyatt Earp. "You're going prospecting? I can't believe it."

Bat's eyes twinkled. Of course he didn't intend to rough his smooth palms grubbing for gold with a pick and pan and shovel. "I'll fill my poke when the stampeders wager their nuggets on the gambling tables at Deadwood."

8. A PISTOL WHIPPING

BAT MASTERSON NEVER REACHED THE GOLD CAMPS OF THE Black Hills in the Dakota Territory. He traveled only as far north as Cheyenne, in Wyoming Territory. The burgeoning town sprawled on a high, wind-swept, grassy plain in sight of the Rocky Mountains. Bat found it another Dodge, only more raucous, with more saloons and gamblinghouses. Although the air was bracing, sweet with the perfume of sun-ripened wild grass, and cooled by distant snow-capped peaks, Bat preferred the smoky atmosphere of the Mint and other places.

Suppliers were touting Cheyenne as the gateway to the Black Hills gold fields. Gold! Men talked of nothing else day and night. Large parties of prospectors pushed North. They were armed against savage forays from the dreaded Teton Sioux. The fierce warriors were determined the white man should not desecrate *Paha Sapa*, the sacred pine-studded gold-pocked hills, home of *Wakantanka*, Great Spirit.

For months Bat remained at Cheyenne. He thrived on bustle, crowds, excited talk, feverish gambling, twenty-four-hour-a-day flux and froth. He hallooed onetime hunters, skinners, soldiers, and former Dodgeites who passed through on their way to the bonanza diggings. As he guessed, dealing faro was bonanza enough for him. In August he wrote Jim and Wyatt Earp, "You're missing a good bet. Come on out here."

Early in the fall Cheyenne braced against its first blizzard. For two days the wind shrieked, and sleet scoured the crude streets. The mud froze in icy ruts. Potbellied stoves radiated heat, but few buildings were warm. Bat shivered as the cold nipped his back, his feet, even his hands. Cheyenne stores were bulging with miners' tools and staples. Not one stocked handsome wool capes, fit attire for a young faro dealer with expensive tastes in clothing. Other gamblers unconcernedly donned large black shawls.

"I wouldn't be caught dead wearing old-woman garb," Bat exclaimed. Besides, shawls reminded him of the poverty-stricken years when his mother's only warm outer garment was a shawl, used also to swaddle infants or cover napping sons.

"Is the weather this cold all winter?" he asked one of the merchants.

The man laughed. "This ain't cold. Wait till the mercury goes to forty below, and the snow piles in twenty-foot drifts."

Bat digested the thought. "Not for me!" Within hours he had packed his valises and was headed back to Dodge. At Sidney, Nebraska, he ran onto Dakota-bound Wyatt and Morgan Earp.

"Better turn back unless you want to spend a miserable winter," he advised. But the Earps were determined, and Bat knew better than to waste his breath arguing. "How is Dodge?"

"Quiet."

"I'll bet. How was Jim?"

"Fine. That boy is a real scrapper," Morgan said admiringly.

"Somebody try to gun him?" Bat asked worriedly.

"Didn't have the chance," Wyatt answered flatly.

After the Earps departed, Bat fretted. He didn't like the idea of Jim's being in Dodge without him to back him up. Not even Wyatt could have told Bat that his younger brother could take care of himself. The feeling of looking out for his brother was strong in Bat. He took pride in being the older, more experienced, the better shot. He liked his role of protector, though he had to admit that so far Jim had never asked his help.

As Bat journeyed on to Dodge City he did considerable thinking. While Dodge remained a major cattle-shipping point, the town would prosper. Bat knew how profitable some businesses were, particularly respectable gamblinghouses. Even the Ford County *Globe* stated: "We believe that what is known as 'square games' are among the necessary belongings of any town that has the cattle trade. We don't believe there are a dozen people in Dodge who seriously object to this kind of gambling so long as this is a cattle town."

Years later Bat wrote, "Gambling was not only the principal and best-paying industry of the town, but was also reckoned among its most respectable."

A few days after returning to Dodge City, Bat bought an interest in the Lone Star, a combination gamblinghouse and theater. The business increased immediately as many men flocked to play cards with a famous gunfighter and frontier hero. There is no record that any ever tried to pick a fight or "showcase" (cheat) him.

At Christmastime Bat and Jim took the cars, as the train was called, to Wichita. Both wore expensive suits and bowler hats, but only Bat sported a satin-brocaded vest, diamond stickpin, and diamond ring. His boots were hand-made of the finest leather, with the wide, high heels he needed for extra height.

After a spending spree the two rented a wagon and team for transporting their gifts to the family homestead. They reined up in front of the farmhouse, now sporting a porch and front door with colored window glass. Ed bolted out and nearly pumped their arms off their shoulders. Tommy, grown tall and slat-thin, cleared the steps in one leap and joined in the welcome. Drawn by the shouts and laughter, Nellie and Minnie stepped shyly onto the porch. Their dark hair was braided back so tightly that their eyes slanted. When Bat spied them, he raced up the steps, grabbed each under one arm, and swung them round and round. "Plain-looking ducks," he decided privately, "but wait till they see what I bought them."

Father and Mother Masterson appeared in the open door. Bat's first thought was, How old and tired they look! And no wonder! More than twenty years of farming, and only lately some prosperity. "Welcome home, boys!" both greeted their sons. Bat embraced his father, and swung his mother off her feet. "Hello, Ma! Did you miss me?"

"Home is like gingerbread without ginger, with you gone," she admitted, her cheeks pink. Then she hugged Jim.

"No lickings for staying away so long?" Bat teased her.

Mrs. Masterson dabbed at her eyes with a corner of her starched apron. "No such thing." Then she stiffened. "I see you are both wearing guns. Off with them this instant! Ed told me you have to wear them out West, but not here. I can't abide the dangerous things!"

"Yes, ma'am," Bat and Jim answered meekly, and unbuckled their belts.

The reunion was as lavish as Bat had dreamed long ago. There were lengths of dress materials for his mother and sisters, and lockets and rings, storemade cloaks, bonnets, and muffs. For his father and Tommy, Bat purchased fine

Winchester rifles with hand-carved stocks. For the whole family there was a new contraption called a Stereoptican Viewer, with a hundred photographs of enchanting, faraway places. One of the high points of the visit was an evening spent at Kown's place, regaling the old friend with tales about Adobe Walls and the Indian campaign.

Soon Bat's fingers began to itch for cards. His restless feet wanted to be traveling. Also, Jim had used up his leave as deputy under City Marshal Larry Deger. So three brothers returned to Dodge—Ed went along. Mrs. Masterson charged Bat with all-too-familiar instructions: "Don't you let nothing bad happen to Ed."

"I won't," he promised.

The next six months were fairly quiet. Bat and Ed worked hard and profitably at gambling. Jim had no trouble deputizing until the first flood of cowboys hit Dodge for the 1877 season. City Marshal Deger, all three hundred and seven pounds of him, refused to control the shootings, brawling, and destruction of property. Bat patrolled Jim's shift with him until Wyatt Earp answered the Mayor's call for help.

As a deputy City Marshal, independent of Deger, Earp once more brought law and order to Dodge. He named both Jim and Ed as deputies, along with Bill Tilghman and Neal "Skinny" Brown, so thin he could not wear gun belts and had to carry his six-guns in shoulder holsters. These men had the cooperation of Ford County's genial sheriff, Charlie Bassett, who promptly hired Morgan Earp as his deputy. Whenever Bassett needed an extra man, he deputized Bat. All top gunfighters, these eight men kept Dodge and the county orderly without clamping down so hard that the cowboys took their business elsewhere.

However, numerous cowboys sported lumps on their foreheads, courtesy of Bat Masterson, when they tried to hurrah the Lone Star. Others, including fat Larry Deger,

lost money gambling there, though the Lone Star was
widely known as a creditable house. Bat's reputation was
such that none would risk a personal encounter with him.
Yet many hoped for a chance to give him his comeuppance.

One afternoon Bat strolled along Front Street, satisfied
with his newest vest of ivory brocade, the perfect background for a heavy gold watch fob studded with diamonds.
He liked the hot weather. His hip didn't ache so much, and
his limp was scarcely noticeable. He had discarded winter-
weight boots for the finest patent leather slippers with
pointed toes, which he kept mirror-bright. Although the
soles were paper thin the shoes had concealed lifts, so Bat
looked almost six feet tall.

Bat walked along, greeting someone every few steps.
Then he noticed a commotion up ahead. He saw Deger kick-
ing a little bandy-legged rooster of a fellow known as Bobby
Gill. Bat snorted. He knew Bobby as a harmless, slightly
addlepated character who delighted in calling Deger well-
deserved insulting names.

The porky Deger, sensing here was an arrest he could
make handily since he outweighed his unarmed, dim-witted
opponent, held Gill by the collar and kicked him mercilessly.

Bat saw red. He rushed forward and clamped an arm
around Deger's neck. When Deger let loose, Bat called,
"Beat it, Bobby!" The little fellow dashed away like a
greased pig.

"Help!" Deger began shouting as he pawed the air.

Half a dozen cowboys lounging against a hitching rail
saw the chance to make trouble for Bat. They came on the
run, pulled him off Deger, and held him, not without difficulty, while Deger beat Bat repeatedly on the head with his
gun. Then he ordered Bat thrown in jail. Bat fought like a
wildcat every inch of the way but soon found himself hauled
before Judge Frost, and fined twenty-five dollars.

"What for?" Bat snapped, since he considered himself innocent of any lawbreaking.

"For fracturing the peace," Judge Frost stated, tongue in cheek.

Bat was about to protest when he remembered two things: first, Deger was still officially the City Marshal, although notoriously inactive and yellow-livered; second, William Barclay Masterson was guilty of "bodily attacking" an officer. An unfriendly judge could have fined him one hundred and fifty dollars and imposed a jail sentence as well. Bat paid the fine speedily and made a beeline for the nearest Tonsorial Parlor.

When Mayor Hoover and the City Council heard how Deger had abused a harmless man and taken unfair advantage of Masterson, they voted to rescind Bat's fine.

Bat pocketed the twenty-five dollars with considerable satisfaction. But it wasn't payment enough for the cuts on his head. If Bat had had one ounce of the killer instinct in him, he would have drawn Deger into a gunfight and killed him, knowing no jury in Dodge City would convict him. But Bat would have nothing to do with this method of revenge so widely used on the frontier. Like Ritter, and the Indians who had stolen his first Sharps, Deger would pay, but not with his life.

Bat figured him for a loudmouth with overweening pride. The man really liked being in a position of authority, not to mention the money made while in office. When Deger filed his candidacy for the office of Sheriff of Ford County, a post with less work, more money, and considerable prestige, Bat went at once to the incumbent, Charlie Bassett. "I'm going to put on a campaign for you that will be the biggest slap in the face Deger ever suffered."

"That's right nice of you," Bassett drawled, "but I'm not going to run for re-election. Why don't you file and run against the big slob?"

Bat grinned. He didn't give two hoots about wearing a
tin star, but what better way to humiliate Deger? "Will you
support me?"

"Sure thing. So will Earp and the Mayor, and lots of folks.
You've got plenty of friends, Bat. You'll be a shoo-in."

Bat nodded. "I've got plenty of enemies, too." Because
he had served as deputy, and had lobbed so many lumps on
cowboys' heads, he knew he would not get the vote of those
in town who felt the cowpunchers should be completely
unhampered in their hell-raising, as long as the millions of
dollars in pay checks was spent each summer in Dodge.

After filing his candidacy, Bat walked to the office of the
Dodge City *Times* and gave this statement for publication:
"While earnestly seeking the suffrages of the people, I have
no pledge to make, as pledges are usually considered, before
election, to be mere claptrap."

An editorial printed alongside Bat's statement read,
"Masterson knows how to gather in the sinners, is qualified
to fill the office, and if elected will never shrink from
danger."

Bob Wright, a founder of Dodge City and a widely
respected businessman, supported Bat: "He is a gentleman
by instinct . . . has a mild disposition until aroused, and
then, for gosh sakes, look out! . . . A most loyal man to
his friends."

In the final weeks of the campaign, personalities were
forgotten. The main issue was law and order versus wanton
license.

When the votes were counted in November, Bat had won
the two-year office as Sheriff of Ford County by three votes.

He was immensely satisfied. In his own mind he could
qualify easily to tackle the three big problems inseparable
from the duties of Sheriff: he was deadly and fast with a
gun; he was popular enough to please those who wanted

law and order, without too badly antagonizing those who did not; he could hunt a man down.

Yes sir, things were very much to his liking, Bat figured as he sketched a design for a fancy gold-plated badge. He would have excitement in this new office, continued profits through his partnership in the Lone Star, and the close companionship of Jim and Ed.

How could the handsomest, best-dressed, successful, popular lawman and gambler ask for more?

9. THE GENIAL SHERIFF

"How do i look?" Bat asked Jim and Ed as he finished dressing in his room at Deacon Cox's Dodge House. He had bought a new outfit for the ceremony of being sworn in as Sheriff.

Jim grinned. "You won't start a fire with that getup."

Bat had taken prolonged ribbing about his gaudy clothes. The association with Earp had benefited him; now he wore black broadcloth suits, a black bowler hat and shoes, white shirt with gold cuff links, soft black silk tie, and a rose brocade vest. His gun belt was businesslike, unadorned leather. The holsters housed forty-five-caliber Colt Peacemakers.

But there was nothing of Earp's self-containment about Bat. He liked crowds; never was alone if he could help it. He was always bubbling with a story or quip. Newspapermen and feature writers who visited Dodge asked to meet him first, and he never disappointed them. Whereas Earp wore his hat squarely on his head, Pat's bowler always sat at a rakish angle. With clear, tanned skin and slightly flushed cheeks, he looked like a fashion plate.

Only twenty-four, his reputation as a celebrity and noted

gunfighter was solidly fixed. No matter that he was credited with at least twenty killings. "Let the drunken man-eating cowboys think that," he said. Without doubt his being known as a killer kept a lot of trigger-happy troublemakers off his back.

His first official act as Sheriff was to swear in as deputies Jim Masterson, Charlie Bassett, and Bill Tilghman. As he figured, with Charlie serving as jailer and Bill as office detail man, he and Jim could have the fun of running down criminals. Since the Earps had left town, the newly elected Mayor, A. B. Webster, had sworn in Ed Masterson as City Marshal. Bat had protested hotly. "You're too good-natured, too easygoing," he warned Ed. "Once these Texans get a snootful of red-eye, they'll shoot at anything."

"Aw, they don't mean any real harm, Bat. They don't scare me."

"Too dang bad they don't!" Bat flared. "Maybe if you did have a good scare, you'd look out for yourself better."

Never forgetting his mother's charge, Bat fretted about Ed. He alerted Jim and the other deputies to watch out for Ed. Although it was not his responsibility, many an evening Bat patrolled with Ed. He put out the word that anyone harming Ed would answer personally to William Barclay Masterson. In his quiet way Jim did the same.

The years at Dodge and Sweetwater had made Bat wise in the ways of troublemakers. Decades later he was quoted as having advised his deputies, "Always keep your gun loaded and ready, but never reach for it unless you are in dead earnest and intend to kill the other fellow. Don't get flustered. Be mentally deliberate but muscularly faster," he added, never having forgotten this advice first given him by Wyatt Earp. "Never try to run a bluff with a six-gun. And the main thing is, if you have to, shoot first and never miss." As an afterthought he warned, "Alcohol and gunpowder don't mix."

When off duty the three brothers were usually inseparable, and obviously enjoyed being together. The respectable matrons of Dodge invited the eligible bachelors to dinners and cotillions. Jim and Ed accepted, but Bat flatly refused. He would attend the Firemen's Ball, and a masquerade sponsored by the Social Union Club. Named a deacon of Reverend Wright's community church, along with Wyatt Earp, he donated liberally to it. Otherwise his social life was centered in the Lone Star. "I have no use for prune-faced choir singers," he quipped. He preferred the vivacious dance-hall girls, yet avoided falling in love with any. He savored freedom more.

Bat got wind of a bare-knuckles boxing match planned to "establish the championship of Dodge." Since prize fighting was illegal in Kansas, Bat was supposed to halt such affairs. Although practically all officers ignored the law, Bat would give no indication of how he would act.

About four-thirty one morning, after the windows at the Saratoga saloon had been shuttered and the piano silenced, Bat strolled through the door. The place was crowded to the rafters. Chairs borrowed from nearly every place in town were jammed ten deep around an improvised ring. Behind these, men were standing on tables, the stage and piano. Bat surveyed the room sternly, though he had to bite his cheeks to do so.

A cowboy near him said, "Aw, Sheriff, you ain't gonna stop the scrap, are you?"

Bat cleared his throat. "Have to. No other choice. It's against the law." Meanwhile he was patting the left side of his coat where his Sheriff's badge usually shone. It was missing. "But if somebody saved a ringside seat for me, I could consider myself off duty."

Laughter and cheers drowned out the suspense. Bat was escorted to a ringside seat.

The Dodge City *Times* described the fight: "During the

42nd round Red Hanley implored the umpire to take Whitman off for a little till he could have time to put his right eye back where it belonged, set his jawbone and have the ragged edge trimmed off his ears where they had been chewed the worst. This was against the rules of the ring so the umpire declined, encouraging him to bear it as well as he could and squeal when he had enough. About the 65th round Red squealed unmistakably, and Whitman was declared the winner."

Thereafter Bat developed an enthusiasm for boxing that was to serve him well in his later years. He also became a devotee of other sports popular in Dodge: cock fighting, horse and dog racing, bull fighting, and baseball. He read the major newspapers, but had little time for books.

Later in January, 1878, the Dave Rudabaugh gang held up the westbound Pueblo Express, of the Atchison, Topeka and Santa Fe Railroad, at Kinsley in neighboring Edwards County. When Sheriff McCause's posse lost track of the gang, railroad officials wired Sheriff Masterson to "go for Rudabaugh." A handsome reward was named. Bat jumped at the chance to prove his worth, and add another facet of glory to his reputation. Naturally he couldn't fail!

Admittedly Bat had the advantage. The gang had fled south across the Arkansas River into country where Bat had hunted buffalo. He knew the region like the back of his hand. Deputizing prairie-toughened ex-buffalo hunters Joshua Webb, Prairie Dog Dave Morrow, and Kinch Riley, Bat hit for Crooked Creek. He left behind his dapper, devil-may-care appearance and attitude. He showed he had not forgotten how to withstand freezing cold, scant food, and long hours in the saddle. He led his men swiftly through a blinding blizzard fifty miles south to Harry Lovell's cattle ranch.

"Any men pass here the last day or two?"

"Nope," Lovell answered, offering them the hospitality of

his cabin and coffeepot. "You run onto two cowboys holed up in some draw?"

"No. You expecting company?"

Lovell shook his head. "They work for me. I been worried since this storm brewed up." Informed the posse was after train robbers, he said, "Don't you go shooting now 'less I tell you it ain't my boys."

Not long after, four men, hump-shouldered against the wind and riding weary horses, came into sight. Bat was all for striding out with guns drawn. Webb, a grizzled veteran of numerous man hunts, snapped, "Quit grandstanding, Sheriff. You want a hide full of holes? Every criminal between Wichita and Dodge knows you. Leave me go out and invite 'em for a cup of coffee. When they git within shootin' range, do as you dang please!"

Spying the riders from a small window, Lovell exclaimed, "Two of those four are my boys. You leave me bring 'em in here." He stepped out of the cabin and approached the riders. He walked with no guns showing and his bare hands at his sides. "Hello, Shorty," he called to one of his cowboys. "Been worried about you." He kept walking. "Hello, Red. Greetings, strangers. Light and have some chuck. Storm's worsening."

"You alone here?" one of the strangers, Rudabaugh, inquired.

"Well, no," Lovell admitted, chuckling in spite of the fact that Rudabaugh had a rifle resting on his saddle, the barrel pointed at him. "There's Mathilda and a new batch of kittens."

Rudabaugh grunted. "Lead the way."

Lovell turned his back on the desperado and led them to his cabin. When their attention was distracted by dismounting, Bat and his deputies stepped out with drawn guns. The robbers surrendered without a fuss.

On the return trip to Dodge, Bat mused, "Say, we can't go back without a good story. How about it, boys?"

Even Rudabaugh was all for the idea. He didn't want folks to know how meekly he had caved in. The deputies suggested how Bat might "fancy up" the account of the surrender. When Sheriff Masterson greeted the press later, he did not disappoint them. The published account, additionally embroidered by the high-blown journalistic style of the day, told of a grim race, a pitched battle, and much daring-do. It was a far cry from the truth. The Sheriff was a hero, and his star shone brighter than ever. None laughed harder at the entire affair than Bat.

Still he proved to be a most effective lawman. As soon as word leaked in of a rustling, or some other lawlessness, Bat set out with two or three trusted men, rode hard and purposefully until he had tracked down the criminal. He always brought the culprit in without having to fire his gun. Jim did not accompany him on these pursuits because he had resigned and left Dodge to take a flier in cattle.

The Ford County *Globe* kept track of Bat's activities. Several items published early in 1878 include:

"A Government train of two wagons and eight mules was raided Tuesday night at their camp on Bluff creek, 37 miles south, eight mules stolen. Sheriff Masterson and Lt. Guard of Fort Dodge, with a couple of men, left Wednesday night in search of the stolen property and captured the thieves."

"Sheriff Masterson and officers captured in the city, Friday last, two horse thieves. . . . The officers of Ford county are on the alert and watch with a vigilant eye every suspicious character lurking in our midst."

"Sheriff Bat Masterson Thursday night arrested one . . . charged with stealing a horse. . . . Sheriff Masterson is an excellent 'catch' and is earning a State reputation."

One day a clerk from Rath's store pounded into the office, shouting, "Three men just robbed the store and headed northeast!"

Inside three minutes Bat and his deputy Bill Tilghman were raising dust on the road. Pushing their horses, they soon overtook the thieves. A few well-placed shots around their heads, and the robbers surrendered. Bat was tickled. This capture was as easy as cutting butter with a hot knife. He ordered the criminals to head for the Dodge lockup.

One of them jeered, "You can't take us in, Sheriff. We're in Edwards County. You got no jurisdiction here."

Bat was checkmated, and knew it. He could not take the two into custody without first riding into Kinsley and getting a warrant from Sheriff McCause. Since McCause had been offended at his going after Rudabaugh, Bat wasn't too anxious to make the personal acquaintance of a fellow law officer whom he did not know. McCause was sure to take offense at Bat's crossing county lines. He thought fast. "Maybe I can't haul you two back to Dodge, but I sure can relieve you of Rath's property. Fork over!"

The thieves emptied their saddlebags. On further prodding, and in spite of their insistence that they had not stolen any jewelry from Rath's, they gave up a gold watch.

"Now get going!"

The thieves departed eastward, and fast.

When Bat returned the articles to Rath's, the proprietor said, "That watch don't belong here, Sheriff."

Bat was astonished, but made a quick recovery. He had robbed the robbers! He pocketed the watch. "It's stolen property, all right. I'll keep it until I find the rightful owner."

Outside he told Bill Tilghman, "Blast it! Now I'll have to track down those thieves again and find out where they stole that watch." It was a fine one, thick as a turnip, the

case elaborately engraved. Bat opened the top of the case.
"No name inside. Oh well!"

About a week later a report came in that three suspicious
characters were camped near the Van Voorhis ranch between Dodge and Spearville, a town well within the limits
of Ford County. Bat hurried off, with Joshua Webb as
deputy.

The cook at the Van Voorhis ranch told him, "Three
strangers been prowling around for days. I think they're
planning to rob the ranch. The boss and his boys are gone
to Ellsworth to pick up cattle. Only me and the handy man
is here. I'd feel better if you picked up them characters."

Bat and Josh circled wide, came in on the fugitives from
behind, and surprised them while cooking a meal.

"Throw 'em up!" Bat ordered.

The three grabbed air, and slowly turned around. With a
jolt Bat realized these were three different men! But they
were rough-looking, needed shaves, and were bowlegged
with the weight of their side arms.

"Clean 'em out!" he ordered Josh.

Webb relieved each of two six-guns, a shoulder gun, and
a knife; picked up their rifles and extra guns from the
saddlebags.

One of the men, a bull-shouldered fellow, demanded,
"Who in blazes do you think you are, taking our guns?"

Leaning on his saddlehorn, with a Colt Peacemaker in his
hand, Bat drawled, "I'm Sheriff Masterson of Ford County.
Who in blazes are you?"

"Sheriff McCause of Edwards County!" the man roared,
his face red with rage. He whipped open his jacket and
displayed his badge.

Bat almost bit his tongue, but his nimble wits did not
fail him. With the graciousness that could charm an owl,
he dismounted, offered his apologies, and explained why

he was man-hunting. He pulled the gold watch from his pocket. "I brought this along to make the thieves confess where they stole it."

McCause's eyes bugged. "That's my watch! Open the back. You'll find my name engraved there." His eyes narrowed. "What are you doing, harboring stolen property?"

Quickly Bat opened the back, which he had neglected to do previously, and handed the watch to its owner. His eyebrows quirked as he said smoothly, "And what are you doing crossing county lines, McCause?"

This time McCause was checkmated. Grumbling, he retrieved his guns, and with his companions lit out hurriedly for Edwards County.

When the men were out of hearing, Bat doubled up laughing. Even Webb's flinty shoulders shook. "If McCause ever finds out I lifted that watch in Edwards County, he'll blow his top."

The story was too good to keep. Bat told it around in his free-swinging style. McCause soon heard it too, but could do no more than grind his teeth.

After several months the Dodge City *Times* editorialized: "Sheriff W. B. Masterson and Deputy William Tilghman are indefatigable in their efforts to ferret out and arrest persons charged with crime. Scarcely a day passes without reward for their vigilance and promptness. We do not record all these happenings, because evil-doing is of such common occurrence. There is a pleasant contemplation in the fact that we have officers who are determined to rid the community of a sore that is a blight upon the well-being of this over-ridden section."

No doubt about it, Bat was deservedly famous and popular. Unlike Earp, he never took himself too seriously. He tried for no records of making arrests. Some culprits needed only a warning to get back on the straight and narrow. He took the spine out of horse stealing and cattle rustling in Ford County. Recognizing that his office carried with it dignity and great responsibility, Bat lived up to those demands.

Yet at this moment of great popularity and happiness, Bat Masterson suffered the greatest tragedy of his life.

10.   ED

WITHIN DAYS AFTER BAT HAD BEEN SWORN IN AS SHERIFF OF Ford County, and had given his deputies and Ed some meaty advice on gunfighting, Ed had a narrow squeak.

Wyatt Earp had left Dodge as soon as the votes were counted and Bat declared winner over Larry Deger. Many cowboys wintered in the cow capital now. With Earp gone and Deger continuing as the do-nothing City Marshal, the cowboys immediately resumed wearing their six-guns inside the city limits. Earp had enforced the ordinance prohibiting this, but Deger lacked the courage to do so. Inside forty-eight hours the Texans were shooting up lamps, windows, and signs, and riding their horses on the planked walks and into Front Street establishments.

At first the Dodge City *Times* editorialized indulgently: "A gay and festive Texas boy, like all true sons of the Lone Star State, loves to fondle and practice with his revolver in the open air. It pleases his ear to hear the sound of this deadly weapon. Aside from the general pleasure he derives from shooting, the Texas boy makes shooting inside the corporate limits of any town or city a specialty. He loves to see the inhabitants rushing wildly around to 'see what all this shooting is about,' and it tickles his heart to the very core to see the City Marshal coming toward him at a distance while he is safe and securely mounted on his pony and ready to skip out of town and away from the officer.

"The program of the Texas boy, then, is to come to town and bum around until he gets disgusted with himself, then to mount his pony and ride out through the main street, shooting his revolver at every jump. Not shooting to hurt anyone, but shooting in the air, just to raise a little excitement and let people know he is in town."

When the townspeople protested, the newly elected Mayor Webster removed Deger and appointed Ed Masterson as City Marshal.

Bat was furious. "Why did you accept? You're not cut out for a job like that. You're too softhearted. You even like these Texans!"

"They're good fellows," Ed maintained, smiling. "They don't mean any harm."

"They might mean no harm when they put a bullet through your gizzard, and feel sorry for it when they sober up. But where will you be? In Boot Hill!"

Ed looked hurt. "You think I'd liver out in a tight spot?"

"No!" Bat thundered. "What worries me is there'll be a showdown, and you will give the other fellow the benefit of the doubt a second too long, and he'll outdraw you. You know how cowboys brag they eat marshals for breakfast."

"They didn't eat Earp, or you," Ed reminded his fuming brother. "And I get along fine with them. They like me."

"Everybody likes you. But that's not saying some varmint won't forget it after he's taken on a quart of red-eye and decides he's going to drill that badge you are wearing."

Ed had heard enough. "Let's change the subject. I'm twenty-five years old. I didn't shake Ma's apron strings to come to Dodge and be henpecked by a younger brother."

Bat changed the subject, vowing privately to watch over Ed as much as was humanly possible. Underneath the gentleness Ed was quietly stubborn, Bat knew. Since boyhood Ed had been a genius at avoiding arguments or quarrels without seeming weak-spined, yet managed to end up having his own way. Although exasperated, Bat could not be cross with him. But it wasn't easy to resign himself to the fact that Ed would conduct himself as he pleased.

Ed's way was to allow "those kids," as he referred to the cowboys, to go on wearing their guns. Because he was so well liked, he was able to quiet most of the rambunctiousness and quarreling with a word of caution. He rarely drew his gun to buffalo a troublemaker. When patrolling with him, Bat often resorted to warning shots or buffaloing; but not Ed.

The horseplay worsened. The Dodge City *Times* editorialized against leniency with gunplayers. Mayor Webster was quoted in the Ford County *Globe:* "Some of the boys in direct violation of the city ordinance carry firearms in our streets without being called to account for it. They do so in such an open manner that it does not seem possible that our city officers are in ignorance of the fact."

Several days later, however, the *Times* lead story was as fine an example of frontier reporting as was ever published:

"Last Monday afternoon, one of those little episodes which serve to vary the monotony of frontier existence occurred at the Lone Star dance hall, during which four men came out some the worse for wear, but none, with one exception, being seriously hurt.

"Bob Shaw, the man who started the amusement, accused Texas Dick, alias Moore, of having robbed him of forty dollars, and, when the two met in the Lone Star, the ball opened. Somebody, foreseeing possible trouble and probable gore, started out in search of City Marshal Ed

Masterson, and, finding him, hurried him to the scene of the impending conflict.

"When Masterson opened the door, he descried Shaw near the bar with a huge pistol in his hand and a hogshead of blood in his eye, ready to relieve Texas Dick of his existence in this world . . ."

Instead of drawing his gun as a deterrent, as Earp or Bat would have done in such a situation, Ed walked up to Shaw. "Come on, now. Simmer down. Let me have your gun."

Shaw spewed profanity that thickened the already smoky atmosphere. "Keep your nose out o' this, Marshal, or I'll plug you too."

The *Times* story continued: "Officer Masterson then gently tapped belligerent Shaw upon the head with his shooting iron, merely to convince him of the vanities of this frail world. The aforesaid reminder upon the head, however, failed to have the desired effect, and, instead of dropping, as any man of fine sensibilities would have done, Shaw turned his battery upon the officer and let him have it in the right chest."

Ed gasped as the bullet grazed a rib, passed around his chest, and emerged under his shoulder blade. The pain was excruciating. Ed felt his fingers slacken around his gun. Even as he began tottering, his left hand covered his revolver. He shot Shaw in the arm and leg. Shaw fired back, but hit Texas Dick; fired again and hit a bystander, before slumping to the floor. Meantime Ed caught the bar with his elbow, steadied himself, and with great courage held off Shaw's friends at gunpoint until assistance arrived.

All this happened so quickly that Bat, his leisurely meal at Kelley's interrupted by hearing someone shout outside, "They're killin' the Marshal at the Lone Star," arrived only in time to help Ed to the doctor.

Though painful, miraculously the wound proved not

dangerous. Bat saw that Ed had the best of care. Not until he was recovering did Bat give vent to his feelings. "I warned you not to let a gun slinger get the draw on you. If I thought you'd let it happen again, I'd run you out of town. And don't think I couldn't!"

"Once was enough," Ed assured him. "It won't happen again."

"You'd be a darn sight better off selling cattle in Wichita like Jim."

"I happen to like being Marshal."

So that was that, Bat realized reluctantly.

However much he wanted to, he could not be with Ed every waking moment. After all he was Sheriff, and a diligent one. He took off on another man hunt, which resulted in his apprehending two robbers named Dugan and Green.

"You sure buttoned that one up in a hurry," Ed congratulated him.

Bat didn't say he had done so purposely in order to return to Dodge and look after a too-good-natured older brother.

The evening of April 9, 1878, Bat was relaxing at the Lone Star. The town had been quiet. For the moment he was not worried. Ed had hired a good man as Assistant Marshal, Nat Haywood. The two were making their rounds.

As Ed and Nat strolled in and out of the amusement places on Front Street, they heard shouting and shots from across the tracks. Ed took off on a high lope, his long legs quickly covering the distance from the Deadline to the trouble spot, a saloon. Haywood trailed him by seconds.

When Ed entered, he recognized a well-known loud-mouthed cowpoke named Jack Wagner. Wagner was intoxicated, and terrorizing the place with rough talk and haphazard shooting. Ed walked right up to him. "Better let me have that gun before you get in real trouble."

Wagner peered at him through bleary eyes. "Oh, 's you, Marshal. Sure." He surrendered the gun butt first.

"Have fun, but keep the lid on," Ed suggested, giving Wagner a friendly pat on the shoulder. When he saw Wagner's boss, A. M. Walker, nearby, Ed gave him the gun. "Check this gun with the bartender and see Wagner doesn't have it back until he's cold sober."

"All right," Walker agreed.

Since the trouble seemed to be over, Ed beckoned his assistant and the two walked out. They had gone only a few steps when Haywood glanced back. "Somebody is trailing us."

In the shafts of light streaming from the saloon window, Ed saw that Wagner and Walker were behind them and that Wagner had his gun in hand. Without hesitation Ed walked back and said, "I told you not to let Wagner have his gun until he was sober." Then he said to the cowpoke, "Hand over the gun. You can claim it at the office in the morning, if you're sober by then."

"I ain't givin' it up," Wagner answered surlily.

Ed reached for the gun, and the two scuffled. Walker jumped in to help his cowboy. Some of their friends had emerged from the saloon. When they saw Haywood move to Ed's assistance, they put a gun to his head.

Instead of freezing, Haywood took off like a greyhound toward the Lone Star. One yell, and Bat was sprinting to the trouble spot. He and Nat were within sight when a shot was fired. Bat saw his brother reel back, his clothing afire from the close shot. In one deadly move Bat drew his gun and fired four shots, one on top of the other. Wagner and Walker cried out, and grabbed a hitching rail for support. Bat's shots, and the look on his face as he closed in, sent the others fleeing like rabbits.

Since the shots had been heard along Front Street, men poured across the tracks. Bat shouted for help to carry his now unconscious brother to their room at the Dodge House. While waiting for the doctor, Bat held Ed in his

arms. "You've got to live, Ed. You've got to! I'll never forgive myself for letting this happen."

His appeals were in vain and within moments Ed died.
Frantically Bat called for a mirror to be placed over his
nostrils and lips. When no vapor clouded the surface, he
realized finally that Ed was gone.

Bat was stunned. "This will kill Ma. She will never forgive
me," he kept saying over and over.

Sorrowing friends drew Bat away from Ed, wrapped the
body in a blanket and carried it to the undertaker's.

Ashen, stone-faced, eyes fathomless in their expression,
Bat dragged himself to the door. "Leave me alone," he told
those who wanted to comfort him.

Outside he borrowed a horse and rode to the railroad
office. His hand shook as he wrote out the tragic message to
be telegraphed to his parents. Then he mounted and disappeared for several hours into the darkness.

Not until years later did Bat admit what he did in that
time. He rode out on the prairie, picketed the horse, and
walked off to be utterly alone. Suddenly his shoulders
began to shake. The iron-hard control gave way, and
anguished sobs tore from his throat. He wept long and
hard, where none could see or hear his agony.

While Ed was being carried to the Dodge House, Jack
Wagner, bleeding heavily from a stomach wound, staggered
into another saloon. "Catch me! I'm dying!" he gasped to
the proprietor, clutching the man's arm.

Proprietor Ham Bell, a friend of the Mastersons, shrugged
him off coldly.

Wagner collapsed on the floor and lay untended until
some of his cohorts got up nerve enough to show their faces
and carry him off to the Lane Rooms. He died there almost
with the same breath in which he confessed being the one
who had shot the Marshal. The next morning he was buried
with scant ceremony on Boot Hill.

Walker, suffering three bullet wounds, one in the lung, was carried to his room. He lingered for weeks, but finally succumbed.

All of Dodge went into mourning for Ed Masterson. His funeral was the first attended by almost the entire community. Doors of the business houses were draped in black crape, and all were closed during the hours of the service.

The Reverend O. W. Wright preached the funeral sermon to those who could squeeze into the Firemen's Parlor. At the conclusion of the service the members of the City Council led the procession to the cemetery at Fort Dodge. Ed would not rest with the unfortunates and riffraff of Boot Hill.

Behind the hearse came Bat, bareheaded, his jaw rigid, straight-backed in the saddle, the only member of the family present. Behind him came the sixty-man uniformed force of Volunteer Firemen, and after them a long, long line of buggies and riders.

The Ford County *Globe* filled an entire page with the account, and tributes. The Firemen wore black armbands for thirty days, and insisted on assuming all costs of the burial.

Though none saw him weep, for he buried his loss deep in his heart, Bat never forgave himself for what happened to Ed.

Many agreed when Bob Wright said, "Bat died a little then, I think. He was never quite so devil-may-care after that."

11. NEVER A DULL STRETCH

A SHORT TIME AFTER THE TRAGEDY, THE FULL FLOOD OF cattle and cowboys spilled across the Arkansas. The season was a high point in Dodge City's prosperity. Over two hundred thousand cattle were sold and shipped between April and October. One sale alone of thirty thousand head grossed six hundred thousand dollars for the owner. Of this, he and his riders spent one hundred thousand in high living, reoutfitting, and gambling in Dodge. And this was only one of many such outfits.

Bat tracked rustlers and kept peace among rival cowboys in the tent and blanket camps peppering the county. He boosted his own income by dealing faro when time allowed. Inwardly tortured by Ed's loss, he ached to go home. But the fearless hero of Adobe Walls and the Indian campaign could not face his mother. No record exists of bitterness between them, but it would be years before Bat saw his home again.

Easygoing Charlie Bassett tried to fill Ed's place as City Marshal; but the Texans ran roughshod over him, hurrahing the town nightly. Once more the Mayor called for help. Wyatt Earp returned on May 12, 1878.

Bat welcomed his friend. After expressing sincerely his regrets about Ed, Earp asked, "Jim in town?" On learning that he was not, Wyatt said, "Too bad. I was counting on him for one of my deputies."

Bat's outlook brightened. "Want me to write him?" A little of the ache lessened. He would not be quite so lonesome with Jim around. When Earp nodded, Bat decided to wire Jim. Days later his brother stepped off the westbound express. Behind him was nineteen-year-old Tommy Masterson. Bat whooped with joy. He held Tommy at arm's length. "By Godfrey, you're as skinny as a beanpole. I'll set you up to a steak dinner that will fill out those ribs."

Jim immediately headed for Earp's office to be sworn in as deputy. Tommy carried their gripsacks to the Dodge House. Naturally an older brother who was Sheriff couldn't be allowed to help. For the first time in weeks Bat was smiling. To numerous friends seen on the street he proudly introduced "my kid brother."

"Think I can get a job here?" Tommy asked. "I aim to make my own way."

"I'll put you on at the Lone Star," Bat offered. He would also see that Tommy learned how to handle a six-gun skillfully.

Tommy hesitated. He had had nineteen years of his mother's preaching. "I don't drink or smoke."

"Bad habits, all of 'em! Better not let me catch you weakening," Bat advised. He was feeling better every moment, now that he had someone to watch over.

"Yes, sir!" Tommy promised.

Bat's blood warmed. Tommy's respectful "sir" reminded Bat that he was a big man around town, a celebrity, a hero. Much of the old sparkle glowed again in his slate-gray eyes. The grim line of his jaw relaxed a little.

Because he had been so preoccupied with his brothers' arrival, Bat had not seen a tall, emaciated, light-haired man

with blue eyes and walrus-tusk mustaches step from the
train. Morose ex-dentist and deadly gunman, Dr. John H.
Holliday had arrived to relieve any and all who played
cards with him of their money.

That evening Holliday drifted into the Lone Star in
company with Wyatt Earp. Bat knew Holliday by reputation, but had never met him before. One look in the guarded
cold eyes, and Bat, who knew well how reputations could
be blown up all out of proportion to the truth, readily believed that this man was a conscienceless killer. However,
he wisely kept his feelings to himself. Since Earp indicated
Holliday was a friend, Bat accepted him surface-wise. But
he never sought his company, yet never openly avoided him.

In later years Bat wrote of Holliday, and had his opinion
accepted as authoritative, "He was selfish and of a perverse
nature, characteristics not calculated to make a man popular
on the frontier. I never liked Holliday; I tolerated him and
helped him at times solely on Wyatt Earp's account, as did
many others."

Oddly enough, to somewhat the same degree that Earp
was criticized for his association with Holliday, Bat Masterson drew fire for assisting Ben Thompson when the notorious killer asked for help. Ben had kept Sergeant King's side-
kicks from killing Bat during the shooting scrape in Sweetwater, Texas. Bat felt beholden to him, and did not hesitate
to repay a debt owed.

Ben had arrived with the first cattle drive. Perhaps out of
respect for Bat and Earp, he never got out of line in Dodge.
At least for a while. Usually he dealt faro at the Long
Branch, drank heavily and alone.

But one morning he roused Bat early. "My kid brother
Billy killed a man in Ogallala, Nebraska. He got hurt bad.
The Marshal there is keeping Billy under guard in his hotel
room until he's well enough to hang."

Bat nodded noncommittally. Personally he thought Billy was long overdue for hanging, being far more vicious than Ben. At the same time, however, Bat could appreciate an older brother's concern for a younger one. "You're asking me 'o rescue Billy?"

"Yeah. I know I'm puttin' you on the spot. You're on the ᶠ the law, but—"

ᵤldn't do it for anyone else, and only this once," it clear. "All right, let's go." He reached for his

oled with his hat. "That's the pinch. There's a ᵤt against me in Ogallala for a little scrape I got several years ago. If I show my face, they'll hang with Billy."

traveled alone to Ogallala. There he discovered guarding Billy had been a soldier in Miles's column me Bat found the Germain sisters.

, if it ain't the great Masterson hisself," the guard ᵢd. "Remember me, Gus Myers? I was a sojer for at time you rescued those little gals."

, sure! Glad to see you again, Myers!" Bat answered, he hadn't remembered the fellow at all.

ᵢen keepin' track of you. You sure as heck has made a 'or yourself. I'm a great admirer of yours, Bat."

ll, thanks." Bat settled down to have a long talk with ard, who was flattered. Before long, Bat learned that held a grudge against the good people of Ogallala t having elected him Sheriff. Bat played on the man's ᵢthies. Soon he had him convinced that the prize pay-ould be allowing Billy to escape, and thus depriving ᵢngrateful citizenry of a public execution. Hangings a rather common sport on the frontier.

e two made careful plans.

When the westbound express was about due in, some

hired roisterers started fighting in front of the hotel. Everyone rushed out to watch. Bat and Myers supported Billy
between them, got him out a back door and safely aboard
the train. They rode as far as North Platte, left the train
there, and hid out in the home of Buffalo Bill Cody.
Though Bat never knew the details, somehow Cody was
indebted to Ben Thompson. There was no hesitation about
providing medicine, rest, and sanctuary for Billy until his
big brother arrived. Vowing eternal gratitude, Ben moved
Billy to a Texas hideout. Bat bid both a cordial farewell,
hoping that was the last he would see of either one.

Bat had barely brushed dust off his Sheriff's chair when he
received another appeal for help. Fred Murray, City Marshall of Hays, Kansas, a rough frontier town to the north,
was hiding out.

Soldiers stationed at nearby Fort Hays had a long, disreputable reputation for brawling in the town's saloons.
Wild Bill Hickok, an earlier City Marshal, had had to
resort to gunplay to corral them. When Hickok killed a
couple, every trooper vowed vengeance. Hickok "moved
out," as he preferred to describe his flight, and stayed well
out of the area ever after. Now Murray had made the same
error.

But this was different, Bat felt. The appeal was from a
brother officer. Without hesitation he saddled up and rode
north, led by Murray's confidant, to the Marshal's hideout
in the heart of town.

Murray was depressed, and with good reason. Lieutenant
Philip H. Sheridan had ordered all troops of the Seventh
Cavalry to bring in Murray dead or alive. "They got a
cordon guarding every foot around town day and night."

"I'll get you out," Bat said confidently. He had a light
wagon and fast team brought around at dark. Bat donned
a threadbare coat and battered hat and rubbed dirt on his

face. He stashed his good clothes under the seat. Then he and Murray's friend wrapped the Marshal in a blanket and carried him, prone, out to the wagon. Bat climbed up, picked up the reins, and headed out of town.

"Halt!" Two troopers on patrol stopped him. "What ya got there?"

Bat pulled a long face. "Corpse. My brother."

"Yeah? What 'd he die from?" an officious corporal demanded.

"Smallpox."

The soldiers jumped back. "Get out o' here fast and don't come back!"

Bat obliged. Hours later Murray was in Dodge. He took the first train East, convinced he had best seek a new profession.

Not long after this two citified dudes detrained at Dodge. Neither outlaws nor gunfighters, they were Eddie Foy and his partner, Jim Thompson, song-and-dance entertainers. Still several years ahead of future fame as New York City's favorite Broadway star, Foy was young, brassy, comparatively unknown.

After checking in at Ben Springer's Comique Theater, a combination gamblinghouse and variety hall, Foy and Thompson set out to give Dodge the once-over. Dark hair slicked under bowler hats, celluloid collars and cuffs showing stiffly under their cheap, loud-checked, tightly fitted suits, they strutted along Front Street. Foy wisecracked loudly, poking fun at the town and especially at the cowboys.

Later someone carried word to Earp and Bat, who were having an early-afternoon breakfast. "The boys are plannin' a nasty surprise for this here Foy."

Both lawmen nodded. "Keep within bounds," Earp warned.

"I'll stand by," Bat offered when he heard the details.

The surprise would be carried off outside the city limits and Earp's jurisdiction.

Blissfully unaware, Foy swaggered along Front Street alone the next afternoon. Suddenly he was pounced on by several cowboys, roped securely, hoisted onto a horse, and led away by a grim-faced bunch. Bat joined the "informal necktie party." Cowboy humor was rough and profane, but Foy stood up to it without flinching. He said later that he was determined not to "liver out," or give his tormentors the satisfaction of thinking they were scaring him.

When a noose was fitted around Foy's neck and the long end of the rope tossed over a cottonwood branch, one of the cowboys said, "What ya got to say for yourself, Foy? Better make it good, because it's the last you'll ever say in this world."

Instead of cringing or bleating, Foy quipped, "What I have to say would sound better at the Long Branch."

The cowboys erupted in laughter. "Y're all right!" they judged Foy, almost fracturing his spine slapping him on the back. They untied him and all rode pell-mell for the saloon. Though it took almost every dime he possessed at the time, Foy bought drinks for everyone. He then performed his best number for them, a hilarious skit entitled "Kalamazoo from Michigan." When he repeated the number later at the Comique, which the cowboys pronounced Come-eeque, "I got more applause than ever," he wrote years later in his fascinating memoirs, *Clowning Through Life,* "and we stayed at Dodge all summer."

No one else ever described the atmosphere of the Comique and other similar places as well as Foy did. In 1928 he wrote, "I wish I could present to an audience of today an adequate picture of those old western amusement halls. Writers and artists have tried to do it, the movies have tried it, but all in vain—the sounds are lacking—the songs and patter from the stage at one end, where the show began at eight o'clock and continued until long after midnight; the click and clatter of poker chips, balls, cards, dice, wheels and other devices at the other end, mingled with a medley of crisp phrases 'Thirty-five to one,' 'Get your money down, folks,' 'Eight to one on the colors,' 'Keno!' and 'Are you all down, gentlemen?' and a thousand of other bits representing the numerous varieties of games that were being played, and which, though mostly spoken in a moderate tone, combined to make a babel of sound. . . . When the various stage performances were over, there was dancing which might last until 4 A.M. or daybreak."

Bat took a great liking to Foy's acts, and almost nightly dropped into the Comique. Ben Thompson also frequented the place. One night Ben took offense at one of Foy's jokes. He began drinking heavily, and brooded over the imagined insult. Suddenly he lurched to his feet and barreled his way backstage. Foy, standing in the wings, did not move as Thompson drew a revolver hidden in a shoulder holster. The killer's hand was wobbling as he jeered, "I'm gonna shoot that light out over your head!"

Foy had a strong hunch that Thompson's drunken aim might well hit his head, instead of the light. Instead of the light. Instead of panicking, he stood rock-firm.

Fortunately Bat had seen Thompson go backstage with an ugly look on his face, and followed. A split second before Ben squeezed the trigger, Bat forced his hand upward. The bullet plunked harmlessly into the roof. "You ever draw a gun again in this town, I'll run you out!" he told Ben.

Even Foy was astonished at the way he surrendered the gun and meekly allowed the Sheriff to remove him from the hall. He didn't know that Bat spent the rest of the night talking Ben out of his murderous mood, and did not leave until he was asleep.

But a few evenings later Foy was dodging bullets again in the opening skirmish of a drama considered one of the all-time showdowns between a notorious gunman, Clay Allison, and his targets, Wyatt Earp and Bat Masterson.

12.   CLAY ALLISON

THE SHOWDOWN HAD BEEN SEVERAL YEARS IN THE MAKING. Both Bat and Earp were thoroughly disliked by the Texans because they had buffaloed and jailed too many of the stomping, intoxicated troublemakers. The cattlemen who sold their trail herds profitably at Dodge spent a great deal of money there. They felt they owned the town and should be able to hurrah without restrictions. The hatred intensified in 1878 because Earp and Masterson remained the only two lawmen in the trail towns whom the Texans had not been able to make run for their lives, or to kill.

Bat was not a part of the last-straw event which led to the showdown. Earp, as City Marshal, had jailed and fined two of the biggest cattlemen: Tobe Driskill, oldest of six feisty brothers and boss of a large retinue of cowpokes, and Bob Rachal, one of four brothers who had a large trail force in his employ. That Driskill and Rachal deserved to be punished was beside the point. They considered themselves humiliated, insulted; their "freedom" restricted. By freedom they meant their license to ride roughshod over a community, destroy property and commit murder, and not be called to account for any or all misdeeds.

Lacking the intestinal fortitude to tackle Earp personally, Driskill and Rachal offered one thousand dollars to anyone who would either kill Earp or make him publicly crawl into the woodwork. Earp heard the news with the usual stolid face.

Shortly after, Bat and Earp drifted over to the Comique to hear Eddie Foy. Bat went inside and played a few hands of poker while he waited for the show to start. Being on duty, Earp stayed outside to keep an eye on Front Street. He would be able to hear Foy through the Comique's open door and flimsy walls.

At eight o'clock Foy capered onto the stage and began singing. Earp leaned against a pillar to listen. A man rode by to the end of the street. Earp recognized him as a cantankerous brawler named George Hoyt.

Hoyt wheeled suddenly, spurred his pony, and raced back toward the Comique, firing six shots in rapid succession. Two almost burned Earp's head; all sizzled over the card tables and stage. At the sound of the first shot everybody inside ducked, including Bat and Foy. One bullet put a hole through the comedian's costume but miraculously did not hit him.

Although he ducked, a natural reaction, Bat realized the shots were coming from the outside, and Earp was out there. Bat leaped to his feet, gun drawn, and looked over the batwing door. Hoyt, hampered by a plunging pony, was still trying to lay more shots. Earp's shots were not connecting with the jumping target. Bat began firing and joined Earp. Seeing Bat, Hoyt raced off. Bat and Earp grabbed horses and gave chase. Bat's Colt jammed, but he hauled out his other and fired swiftly until he had to reload. In that brief period Earp shot Hoyt out of the saddle.

A month passed before Hoyt died of his wound. He had

confessed to a deliberate attempt to kill Earp for the thousand-dollar bounty.

Meantime the Texans had decided that the only one who could take care of Earp—and of Masterson, who had had the nerve to assist Earp in shooting that "poor, defenseless boy," Hoyt—was Clay Allison of Las Animas, Colorado. Allison, a handsome six-footer, was a maniacal killer credited with shooting twenty men, six of them Kansas marshals. He had ninety thousand dollars in rewards posted against him for these and other crimes.

"Dog" Kelley got wind of the plot and promptly told the two lawmen, who ate fairly regularly at his place. "Clay is goin' for both of you. Anything I can do to help?"

"Nope," Earp replied.

Bat's grin was not pleasant, and his gray eyes glittered. "Clay is our boy."

He and Earp began talking quietly about how they would handle Allison. Earp was all for meeting Clay head-on in a man-to-man duel. Bat argued against it. He thought his idea was better. "You and Allison are crack shots. In a duel, no matter who draws first, both of you will lose. I say let's curry his hair. Let's make him back down in public. That's the worst that can happen to that varmint."

At first Earp rejected the idea, but Bat kept up the butter-talk until Earp agreed. One of the main parts of the plan was to ignore Allison's arrival, and let him brag his way from one place to another before facing his victims. "He'll talk half the fight out of himself that way," Bat believed.

All of Dodge braced for the showdown. Though Bat and Earp made no outward preparations, friendly businessmen agreed to cover the two of them so none of the Texans could gun them from behind.

One hot August morning Allison and several tough sidekicks arrived. Earp had patrolled until dawn; Bat had

played cards until then; both were short on sleep. Nevertheless they shaved and dressed, taking plenty of time, strapped
on their guns, and met at Kelley's for ham and eggs.

A man sidled up to their table. "Clay is mouthin' off in
the joints across the Deadline. He's callin' you both ugly
names for not showin' yourselves."

Bat showed no reaction to this. "How is Clay togged out?"

Allison liked fancy clothes as much as Masterson. For
the big occasion he had donned black tight-fitting trousers,
a white shirt with black embroidery, a silver-studded belt
and pearl-handled revolvers, black sombrero and black and
white boots. His war horse was creamy-white, the leather
trappings sparkling with silver and glass studs.

In contrast, the two lawmen wore their usual black
trousers, boots, and felt hats, white shirts and unadorned
guns.

As Bat had predicted, the longer he and Earp lingered
over their coffee, the more Allison swaggered. He was
furious at having his presence ignored. He assured everyone
that undoubtedly Earp and Masterson had taken cover.
"Let's root 'em out, boys!"

But first the killer and his backers must fortify themselves
with a drink.

Meanwhile another informant slipped into Kelley's. "Allison is comin' up Second to Front in a minute!"

Bat and Earp parted company. Bat picked up a loaded
shotgun, went out the back door and hurried to Second
Avenue, which bisected Front Street. It was Dodge's main
intersection, the place he had decided as best for the
showdown. As he crossed to the east side and took his place
in a doorway on the northeast corner, he noticed men
lounging against store fronts and peering over rooftops.
Nonchalantly Bat tilted his hat at an angle and readied the
shotgun. Only a shotgun with its deadly scattering shot
could argue effectively where a gang was involved.

The wild bunch appeared, firing their revolvers in the air. Then Allison spotted Bat, alone and exposed on three sides. He reined up. His gang halted behind him. Clay's hand went for his gun. But when Bat leveled the shotgun, Clay's hand hung in mid-air. His gang scattered like quail, leaving him alone and exposed at the intersection.

Bat thumbed back the hammer, and waited.

Allison licked his lips. He seemed frozen, but Bat could hear him cursing those who had run out. Drops of sweat trickled off his chin. Slowly he laid his gun hand on the saddlehorn. "I'll take care of you later," he sneered.

Bat put the shotgun down and dropped his hands. "Glad to oblige you right now, Allison."

"Where is Earp?" Clay demanded, pointedly ignoring Bat's challenge.

Bat nodded. Allison looked west up Front Street. It was deserted.

Bat saw Allison was upset. The strategy was paying off! Allison had not anticipated containment. He hadn't expected to meet Bat first and alone when actually Earp was his main target. He had expected a swift attack; an even swifter finish in his favor. But nothing was going according to Clay's plan, or brag.

Allison brought his pony to the hitching rail at the corner, and dismounted carefully. Wright and Beverly's entrance was there. "If Earp is in there, I'll smoke him out!" he shouted for all to hear, and stomped inside. But he came right out. No Earp there.

He entered the Long Branch next door. Earp wasn't there either. The Texans were not offering to help, not while Bill Harris, Chalk Beeson, and Luke Short had shotguns trained on them.

Allison spun around, stepped outside, and almost tripped over Earp. He grabbed for time. "You Wyatt Earp?" He noticed Earp's hands dangling loose.

"I am."

Allison stuck out his chin and glowered, "I been looking for you." He stepped closer so Earp could not see his right hand working for his gun.

"You've found me."

Allison had his Colt half out of the holster when suddenly his hand shot in the air. Bystanders peering from every vantage point of cover were as astonished as Allison to see Earp's gun poking Clay in the ribs. The Marshal had drawn with incredible swiftness.

Allison tried to stare Earp down, but failed.

He cleared his throat and said, "I'm going around the corner."

"Don't come back."

Allison backed to the corner. He was perspiring freely. Suddenly he ducked into Wright's.

Bat laughed and called to Earp, "He's gone in to grab a drink and bolster his courage."

Earp remained grim-faced. Bat continued guarding the intersection. Luke Short came out of the Long Branch with a spare shotgun to help Earp. "This is my play." Earp stayed him without taking his eyes off the corner.

"Charlie Bassett is coverin' you from the rear," Short informed the Marshal, eliminating any ambush from that direction.

Finally Allison reappeared, mounted, and shouted from the corner, "Come here, Earp. I got something to say to you."

"I can hear you," Earp answered. He was standing slightly spraddle-legged, his guns holstered. Both thumbs were hooked in his belt, the fingers splayed back toward the gun butts.

From behind Allison, Bat saw several Texans sidle out of Wright's, hands sneaking toward their guns. "Drop 'em!" he shouted, tossing the revolver to his left hand and leveling the shotgun at them. Several guns smacked into the dust.

Seeing this, Allison began to curse again. They were supposed to back his play; to have others covering every angle in town; to cut down Masterson while he personally took care of Earp.

The Texans bleated, "Masterson got the drop on us."

Allison raked his spurs and rode pell-mell for the bridge. There he wheeled savagely, brandished his gun, and faced the intersection. "You stay out o' this, Masterson! I'm goin' for Earp."

Earp ran lightly to the intersection. "Come on, Clay. Either shoot or shut up!"

Allison whooped and rode down on Earp. When he was some fifty yards away, Earp leveled his six-gun but held his fire.

Allison nearly sawed his pony's mouth in half reining up, wheeled, and raced at breakneck speed across the bridge. This time he did not return.

The big, bold, hired killer had livered out.

The Texans made one more try at a time when they knew Masterson was away on business. This time they would have succeeded if Doc Holliday had not butted in with blazing guns. Only Texans were buried on Boot Hill.

After that, things were reasonably quiet in Dodge City. The Texans brawled and shot among themselves. None made a play for either the Marshal or the Sheriff. But for Bat life was far from dull. He had rustlers and horse thieves enough to keep his job interesting.

Plus the unexpected.

Frank and Jesse James, vacationing from crime, came to Dodge to relax. They started to pick a fight in the Lone Star one evening when Bat was dealing faro. Although it was Earp's place to break it up, he wasn't on hand. Deciding he had a right to protect his own business, Bat moved in fearlessly. He convinced the two that neither the Lone

Star nor Dodge itself was the place to cut up. "I've bucked tougher birds than you," he told Jesse, the ringleader. "Keep the lid on, and you can stay in town as long as you like. Make trouble, and I'll settle your hash plenty."

Jesse took time to think, and decided he didn't want to spoil his vacation. He and Frank and their bunch caused no further ruckus in Dodge.

In September a youthful Texan, not yet twenty, paid off after punching cattle up the trail, made a beeline for a saloon to wash the dust from his throat. Bat happened to be coming along Front Street when the cowboy dismounted and stomped into the Long Branch. In violation of the arms ordinance, he was so weighted down with ammunition and six-guns that he walked bowlegged. Amused, Bat stepped inside to watch. The kid began pouring red-eye down his throat. He grew bolder with each raw swallow, and began bragging about what a tough hombre he was. "By Godfrey, the lawmen in Dodge has been roughin' up my friends too dang much. Wait till Billy Donaldson meets up with 'em," he threatened. He waved a gun in his wobbly hand.

When none of the men standing around paid any attention to him, Billy directed more personal insults at them.

Bat realized the youngster was likely to be shot down if he kept up such antics. No need to bother Earp. He walked up to Billy, wrenched the gun out of his hand, and buffaloed him with it.

Billy came to after a few moments and staggered to his feet. Bat gave him a tongue-lashing that took the brag out of the youngster. Then Bat completely disarmed him. "You can call for these at the Marshal's office in a year or two, providing you're still alive. Now get out of town in five minutes or I'll march you to jail!" Billy slunk out and rode away.

A few evenings later Bat was coming along Front Street

when he saw a dust-covered rider haul up. The man dismounted, slapped the dust off himself, then peered up and down the street.

"Looking for someone?" Bat asked pleasantly.

The stranger towered above Bat. "Yes. A guy named Masterson."

Bat rubbed his nose thoughtfully. "Haven't seen him since morning," he lied smoothly, his eyes beginning to sparkle.

"You know him well enough to deliver a message for me?"

"I sure do. Glad to oblige you, stranger."

The man poked a finger into Bat's chest. "You tell Masterson that Tom Donaldson is gonna beat the livin' daylights out o' him, so after this he will leave my kid brother, and me, and all the rest of us Donaldsons alone!"

Bat pretended to be annoyed. "No sir! Tell him yourself. I got something to say to Masterson myself."

"You got a grudge against him too?"

"I aim to kill him!" Bat answered convincingly.

Donaldson was disappointed. Suddenly he brightened. "Toss you for it."

Bat pulled a coin from his pocket. "Your choice, stranger." "Heads."

The coin came up tails.

"Dawgonnit!" the Texan grumped. "I ain't gonna let you do it all. Let's us both go for Masterson. You take the first shot. If you miss, I'll let him have it."

"Fair enough! But let's have a drink first."

The two walked into the Long Branch. Over drinks Bat asked, "What did Masterson do to you Donaldsons?"

"My kid brother and me, we come up the trail with cattle. We're layin' over at a tent camp a ways from town. My kid brother came to town to have some fun. He was mindin' his own business when this Masterson come along and, for no reason at all, pistol-whupped Billy to a pulp."

"That so?" Bat chirked. "Say, I remember that business

But you got it wrong. Your kid brother was asking for trouble." Bat gave a true explanation of Billy's account. "Instead of gunning for Masterson, you should be grateful. He saved Billy's life."

"Oh." Donaldson digested the story. Then his eyes narrowed. "How come you know so much about this?"

"Because I'm Bat Masterson. And if you don't want Billy buried on Boot Hill, keep him away from guns until he grows up!"

Donaldson was disgusted, rather than offended. "I should 've knowed the kid wasn't telling the truth. He's too almighty big for his britches. You willin' to accept my apology, Masterson?"

Bat grinned. "I'll even buy you another drink. And you can pick up Billy's guns at the Marshal's office." They parted friends.

After that incident life went on at a more even tenor for Sheriff Masterson. He still made Ford County too hot for rustlers and horse thieves, dealt faro when time allowed, enjoyed any and all sporting events, watched over his brothers, and lived every moment to the hilt. Although he could not know at the time, the year 1878 was to be the great year—the climax of Bat's long and varied career.

In 1878 vast herds moved through Dodge's shipping corrals, but the Texans kept their high jinks within bounds. However much Earp and Masterson might think they were entirely responsible for the change, other factors were involved.

Dodge City was growing up, becoming more civilized. Gradually the hoodlum element lessened, and the remnants stayed below the tracks. More and more respectable women, wives with children, were seen in Front Street's general stores. The Lone Star, the Long Branch, Kelley's, and other places prospered, but more as all-male clubs. With their hot blood and feistiness thinned out by several trail trips, the cowboys began staying sober long enough to view the grassy plains of western Kansas with more than jaundiced eyes. They were ready to settle down to ranching, marriage, civic responsibility.

The Ladies' Aid took over the main block of Front Street for an outdoor fair, bazaar, and dance. Those who attended danced not to bullets but to a fiddler and pianist. Chinese lanterns glowed like flowers below bullet-riddled signs. Ice-cream socials, church and organization dinners, musicales, a club that was forerunner of a later-day Chamber of Commerce—all had their impact. Dodge's permanent citizens worked hard to rid it of its reputation as the wickedest town in the West.

Then a rich new gold and silver strike in Arizona drained off those who craved excitement. Jim and Morgan Earp were among the first to leave. Another brother, Virgil, wrote that he had located a mine near Prescott, and that other mining bonanzas were to be had at the newest camp, named Tombstone. Wyatt stayed only long enough to sell the property he had bought in and around Dodge. On September 9 the Ford County *Globe* carried the following item: "Wyatt Earp, the most efficient marshal Dodge City ever had, has resigned and is leaving for Arizona."

Then Doc Holliday left. Bill Harris and Luke Short sold their interest in the Long Branch. Tombstone looked better for a gamblinghouse.

Bat thought about making the change, but Jim and Tommy wanted to stay in Dodge. The Lone Star was still making money. The Independent political party was urging him to run again for Sheriff.

When Bat announced his candidacy for re-election, the Dodge City *Times* lined up behind him: "Bat is acknowledged to be the best sheriff in Kansas. . . . He is the most successful officer in the state, immensely popular and generally well liked. Horse thieves have a terror for the name of Masterson. He will be elected by a heavy majority."

The opposing People's party named George Hinkle, bartender, on their ticket. Hinkle was no gunfighter, had no experience in any kind of office. It looked as if Bat was a shoo-in.

Then the Texans banded together. They decided that, if they poured enough money into buying votes for Hinkle, they could defeat Masterson. They had waited a long, long time for revenge.

Bribery and free beer won the election for Hinkle. Bat lost by one hundred and thirty-six votes.

He was furious. "That's gratitude for you! To blazes with this town! Let the Texans have it as long as they've bought half the men in town anyway. I'm through risking my neck and being the target for every drunken gun-toter just so people can walk the streets here without being run over or shot."

Jim and Tommy tried to quiet him, but this was Bat's first real defeat. It put a big dent in his self-esteem. "I'm leaving. Are you coming with me?"

"No," Jim answered. "I'm not mad at anybody. The new Mayor is going to name me City Marshal. I'm staying here."

Rather than choose between Jim and Bat, Tommy replied, "I'm going back home. I want to be a farmer from now on."

Slamming his belongings into his gripsacks, Bat took the first train out of town.

13. TOMBSTONE

BAT DETRAINED AT KANSAS CITY. FOR MONTHS HE LIVED THE life of a celebrated gunfighter and gambler. Perhaps he visited his family. When Kansas City palled, he visited St. Louis and Chicago.

A letter from Wyatt Earp caught up with him. Gambling concessions were big business in Tombstone, Earp reported. Property values were skyrocketing. A man could hardly lose on mining investments. "During my first month as Deputy Sheriff of Pima County, I netted over seven hundred dollars in fees from arrests."

Bat read between the lines. Then he thought back over the past months. He had no complaints, save one: life was too easy! He was restless, growing soft, pale-faced. Living off a hero's reputation was all right if a man could stomach a soft diet. But he had always preferred rare beefsteak and peppersass.

He missed the keen-edged zest, the constant challenge, the exhilarating purposefulness of serving law and order in Dodge. Could he recapture that feeling in Tombstone?

He knew the bare bones of Tombstone's beginnings. In

August, 1877, a prospector named Ed Schieffelin struck it rich. When his ore assayed twenty thousand dollars to the ton, the stampede was on full blast. Territorial Governor John C. Frémont, a famed explorer but highly incompetent administrator, failed to provide protection for the silver bullion transported to the railhead. Cattle rustlers headed by Old Man Clanton preyed on the shipments. Those who dared accuse them met with untimely "accidents." As yet Earp lacked enough evidence to serve warrants against the gang.

By the time Bat arrived late in January, 1881, two months after his twenty-seventh birthday, several new developments had occurred. Cochise County was carved out of sprawling Pima County, and Tombstone designated the county seat. Johnny Behan was appointed Sheriff; Earp, Deputy United States Marshal. Also, as undercover agent for the Wells Fargo Company, Earp frequently rode as shotgun guard on the stagecoaches in an effort to catch the gang in a robbery. To date no shipment he was guarding had been molested.

When Bat reached the railroad terminus in Arizona, he transferred to a stagecoach for the remaining seventy-five miles to Tombstone. While crossing the blistering mesquite-covered desert country, the coach was almost wholly enveloped in dust. Bat glimpsed little of the San Pedro Valley or the stamp mills and concentrators built to refine the ore mined in the adjacent Mule and Dragoon mountains. But he sensed the upward pull as the teams labored the steep pitch to the camp. His ears popped long before the coach rumbled onto Allen Street and stopped.

The moment Bat's expensive valises smacked the dirt, a small Mexican boy pounced on them. "'otel, señor?"

Bat nodded and flipped him a silver dollar.

Refusing help, the boy lugged the valises inside a flimsy structure.

After paying in advance for a room, and two dollars extra for a bath, Bat changed to summer-weight dark trousers, a clean white shirt and black string tie. He exchanged the bowler for his wider-brimmed black felt hat, strapped on his belt, and snugged the Colts in the holsters. As he ventured forth, his expensive patent-leather shoes rapped smartly on the bare floor. His eyes were bright; his hair and mustache glistened with pomade; his step was first cousin to a swagger.

He drifted along the crowded planked walk. Allen Street's sixty-foot width was jammed with whipsawed frame buildings, adobe structures, and large tents. Suppliers, gunsmithy, saddlery, assayers, eateries, stables, saloons, and gambling-houses were wall to wall, back to back. Beyond these were sun-blasted hills and mountains chawed with mine holes. Ore wagons crawled over a cat's cradle of roads from the mines to the concentrators.

He worked his way to the Oriental, the largest and fanciest gamblinghouse. Wyatt Earp and Bill Harris, former owner of the Long Branch in Dodge, owned the controlling interest. Another crony, mild-faced but formidable Luke Short, dealt faro for the house. From the entrance Bat noted the mirror-backed bar and brilliant chandeliers, the huge reed ceiling fans waving to and fro to break up the clouds of cigar smoke, the staccato tempo created by feverish card playing and big-money talk.

Harris and Short hallooed. After the usual backslapping and swapping of friendly insults, they moved to a far table. "Wyatt has been wonderin' when you'd turn up," Short said.

"Trouble brewing?" Bat asked, looking hopeful.

Harris nodded. "Our competitors hire bully-boys to rough up our customers. Fast as we throw 'em out, more show. Earp, he's on the jump with this Marshal job and ridin' shotgun. He can't be six places at once."

Bat laughed. "I haven't buffaloed a man for a long time."

Short grunted. "You'll get plenty of practice in this place."

The talk turned to business. Bat agreed to deal for the house and serve as trouble shooter. Being a celebrity, he would draw the crowds. His talents at buffaloing would insure orderliness.

When Harris excused himself, Bat asked Luke, "Now bring me up to date on Earp."

"He's pointin' for real trouble," the sawed-off gambler admitted in a low voice. "There's this gang: Old Man Clanton and his boys, the McLowery brothers, Johnny Ringo, and Curly Bill Graham. They've rustled all the cattle and burnt out their competitors. Now they're goin' for the silver. They rob a stage and Sheriff Behan don't even send out a posse! Wyatt, he's pointin' for the lot of 'em."

"He'll need help."

Short agreed. " 'Course he's got Morgan and Virgil, and Doc Holliday."

Bat felt his pulse quicken. If Earp needed help on the side of the law, Bat would oblige, and welcome! Dodge or Tombstone, someone had to ramrod the law down the throats of thieves and murderers. And who was more expert at this than Earp and Masterson?

Soon Earp appeared, crossing the floor in his lithe, long-limbed stride.

Bat extended a hand. "Hello, Wyatt!"

Earp's long fingers gripped Bat's momentarily. He sat down and knuckled back his black hat. "Luke, think you can rustle two steaks?"

Short took the hint and left. Quickly Earp briefed Bat on the Tombstone situation. It was incredibly complex, the evil concentrated, the stakes enormous, with Earp almost single-handedly trying to bring a pack of curs to heel. More than an hour passed before Earp said in parting, "Dodge was a church picnic compared to Tombstone."

And that's all right with me, Bat thought as his friend departed. Already he could feel his stomach muscles tightening.

That evening he started dealing poker. He noticed a tough-looking character enter. From Sweetwater to Dodge to Tombstone, the hired toughs were alike: big-mouthed, with a get-out-of-the-way stride; shoving out their jaws; working hard at looking fierce; squint-eying for some weakling to shove around. Wish I had a dollar for every one I've buffaloed, Bat thought.

When the stranger beelined for Short's table, Bat laid down his cards. "A short recess, gentlemen?" As he cut across the crowded floor he heard the fellow accusing Short of cheating. Bat collared him and booted him all the way out to the street. Returning inside, he ran smack into Luke.

"Let me at him!" Luke roared, livid with rage.

"Forget it. He was drunk. He won't be back."

"Yeah? Well, who's that comin' through the door?"

Bat whipped sideways just as a bullet streaked past his belt buckle, burned Luke's shirt cuff, and hit a supporting post. Luke fired once and killed the man outright.

Bat mopped his face with a fine white handkerchief. That had been close!

Yet he remained suave and dapper, his eyes wary and slate-colored. He conducted a scrupulously honest card game, tolerated no interference, and prospered. He saw little of the much-involved Earp, and even less of Doc Holliday.

He took time to write a colorful letter about the Tombstone situation to his younger brother Jim, still in Dodge City.

Jim answered, "You sure can deal words off the top of the deck. Bet Earp is glad to have you around. Dodge hasn't changed any. I had a run-in with Peacock. Demanded he fire Al. I'm sure Al is cheating me. P. drew his gun. I did same. We both missed. Tommy wrote everyone at home well and hoping for a good crop. Yours, Jim."

Before Bat left Dodge, and against his advice, Jim had bought an interest in a dance hall operated by A. J. Peacock and his brother-in-law, Al Updegraff. In Bat's estimation the two were crooks.

"Aw, you don't like them because they're campaigning against you," Jim had flared. "I'm old enough to run my own life. Quit fussing over me like a nervous hen."

Bat clammed up. At the time he was confident of being re-elected. He was equally positive no man would risk his enmity by harming Jim.

But after Bat left Dodge in a huff, apparently Peacock and Updegraff started fleecing Jim. That Peacock dared draw against Jim angered Bat. But learning Jim had drawn and *missed* was intolerable! Bat wrote a scorching I-told-you-so reply. Jim's poor shooting was "downright humiliating to me. Don't let it happen again."

Bat also wrote several cronies at Dodge. He lined out what he, personally, would do if either Peacock or Updegraff didn't do right by Jim. The cronies would air his warning; the crooks would hear about it, and thereafter be disinclined to deal unfairly with ex-Sheriff Masterson's brother. Quite sure he had protected his brother's interests, Bat worried no further.

February slipped by with no trouble from any quarter. In mid-March several of the Clanton gang pulled a boner. Masked and wearing rope wigs, they attempted to rob a stagecoach carrying a fortune in bullion. Bob Paul, riding shotgun, held them off at first, but not before their shots killed the driver and a passenger. The teams bolted, forcing the bandits to give chase in the bright moonlight. Their masks slipped. Paul recognized them before he forced their retreat. Then he retrieved the lines and raced the stage safely into Benson. He wired Earp from there.

Earp immediately deputized Morgan and Virgil, Bat and Wells Fargo Agent Williams. As the posse filled saddlebags, Earp said, "We'll be some time getting back. Fill your canteens."

Bat had donned cotton drill trousers, a heavy shirt and tent-cloth jacket. He relished being in the saddle at dawn, with the sun shooting up behind the mountains like a brass band. He needed fresh air and exercise. After an hour's hard riding his shirt was soaked with perspiration. He knotted a handkerchief over his nose and set his hat lower to shade his eyes from the glare and dust.

Under a merciless sun the five pushed their man hunt over broken country, along dry river beds. One hundred and fifty miles of hard pursuit, snatching sleep on the desert floor with no thought of lizards or snakes, eating sparsely, using up all the tobacco.

Bat thrived on it at first.

Finally the posse flushed Luther King, who blabbed, "I only held the horses. Bill Leonard, Jim Crane, and Harry Head done the shooting."

Earp was considering hauling King along with them when Sheriff Behan and a deputy rode in sight.

Bat's lip curled. "Funny Behan knew where we were, and what we might find."

"Been trailing us," Earp guessed.

When Behan joined them, he blustered, "What's going on here?"

Earp explained briefly, and Behan said, "King ain't committed no federal offense. He's my prisoner. I'll take him back to Tombstone."

Since Earp lacked evidence actually proving Behan was protecting the Clanton outfit, he realized that letting the Sheriff have King might prove enlightening.

For ten more days the posse scoured the wild country.

On one stretch they were forty-eight hours between water holes. Finally Bat's horse dropped in its tracks and had to be destroyed. Bat rode double with Morgan until they met a teamster headed for Tombstone.

"How much longer are you going to keep going?" Bat asked Wyatt.

"Long as there's one horse on his feet."

Bat threw his saddle and gear into the wagon. The hard plank seat was uncomfortable, the driver no talker. Bat was saddle-sore, parched, filthy; his bad hip ached; his eyes were inflamed; his nose was swollen from sunburn. He looked disgustedly at the bleak landscape. Suddenly he was homesick for green grass. The farmer in him yearned for green pastures and clear creeks.

The wagon poked along to Tombstone. A hot soak and ointment eased Bat's discomfort. The first thing he learned from Luke Short was that Sheriff Behan had allowed Luther King to escape.

"There goes Earp's case against the gang!" Bat chewed a fresh cigar to shreds. "Looks like the only way Earp is going to stop that gang is to have an out-and-out showdown with them!"

Short blinked. "Yeah. Holliday said the very same thing."

Two days later Earp and the others limped in empty-handed. The bandits, furnished fresh horses by ranchers in cahoots with the Clantons, had escaped into Mexico. The ensuing days passed without further open trouble.

At the end of the first week in April, Bat received a telegram. "Jim in danger. Come at once." Dispatched from Dodge City, it was signed "A friend."

An icy hand clutched Bat's heart. Jim in danger? By Godfrey, he wasn't going to be gunned down like Ed! Bat exploded into action.

Though the train was swift for those days, Bat fretted

every stopover, every hour. He regretted leaving Earp, but the Marshal had his brothers and Doc Holliday backing him.

"Jim's got only me."

Thus Bat missed the great showdown when Wyatt, Virgil, and Morgan Earp and Doc Holliday shot it out with Ike and Billy Clanton, Tom and Frank McLowery, and Curly Bill Graham in the gunfight at the O. K. Corral.

Bat had enough on his hands without borrowing trouble. The telegram about Jim was bait to draw him into a lethal trap.

14. BULLETS ACROSS THE PLAZA

SHORTLY AFTER THE TRAIN PULLED OUT OF LAS VEGAS, NEW Mexico, the station telegrapher found a message on his desk, along with money for dispatching it.

In due time at Dodge City, A. J. Peacock received a wire informing him Bat Masterson was headed north to kill him and Updegraff. It was signed "A Friend."

As a dance-hall operator Peacock was no stranger to gunfire. However, a showdown with Bat terrified him. He scurried off to warn Updegraff. The two plotted to stack the odds against their adversary.

The Santa Fe chuffed to a stop opposite the red station at eleven o'clock, Saturday, April 16, 1881. The town loafers let out a whoop as a dapper figure sporting an ivory brocaded vest and bowler hat stepped off the coach.

"Bat!"

"Hi yuh, Bat ol' pal! Welcome back!"

"You settin' up drinks at the Long Branch?"

Bat pushed through them. "Later, boys."

The derby sat firmly over his hard, slate-colored right eye. His unbuttoned coat gave unhampered access to a

148

single holstered Colt .45. "Traveling insurance," he called it, all a respectable businessman needed in towns like Kansas City or Chicago, or while touring. His other artillery was in his valise.

He planned to go straight to Jim's room at the Dodge House. If Jim was all right, the two would call on Peacock and Updegraff. But if Jim was not all right, Bat would start dealing trouble. Frontier law permitted a man to extract payment for wrong committed against himself or his family.

Bat stepped off the splintered platform. His heels gouged sharp patterns in the dirt as he strode down the slight embankment formed by the elevated track bed. He started across wide, rutted Front Street. Dodge City boosters pretentiously called this wind-swept, ugly, littered frontage the Plaza. It was utterly devoid of anything that might serve as cover from the elements, or gunfire. No traffic obstructed Bat's course.

His sharp eyes picked up Peacock and Updegraff emerging from a saloon. They started across the roadway. "Hold up! I've got something to say to you two!"

Peacock and Updegraff suddenly unleashed several shots apiece. Then they raced across the tracks and took cover behind a calaboose parked on a siding.

"What in blazes—" Drawing his six-gun, Bat gave chase. Then bullets began screaming past his head. *Rifle* bullets. *From behind.* Caught in a cross fire, he threw himself down on the embankment and fired two shots at Peacock and Updegraff. They splintered the corner of the calaboose. Peacock ducked; poked his head out, fired hastily, and ducked again. Updegraff did the same.

Bat shielded his eyes from the dirt spurting as bullets creased the ground. He was in a tight spot. The two men had deliberately raced across the tracks so Bat's back would be turned to Front Street. From half a dozen doorways men were taking shots at Bat.

But only for a few seconds. Men boiled onto the boardwalk. Neal Brown and other friends of Bat recognized the
derby-hatted figure prone in the dirt. They dived into the
Long Branch, and emerged with shotguns. The Plaza was
laced with lead. Horses pitched wildly at the hitching rails;
glass tinkled; signs quivered as bullets ricocheted.

Bat fired as a hat brim showed from behind the calaboose.
He shredded it. He fired again, and twice more. Then the
hammer clicked against an empty chamber. With no clip
of extra cartridges, he was defenseless.

Updegraff showed his face. "We know your gun is empty!"
He stepped out and took careful aim. But before he could
shoot, he crumpled from a bullet fired along Front Street.

"Stop firing! Lay off! Throw down your guns!"

Mayor A. B. Webster trained his twelve-gauge shotgun
along the firing line. A few ignored his command. Webster
cut loose with a blast. That brought the Battle of the Plaza
to a sudden stop.

Bat got to his feet as the Mayor approached.

"Throw down your gun!"

"No need to," Bat answered. "I'll bring it to you."

"You're under arrest!"

"What for?"

"For discharging a pistol on the streets. It's against the
law. You know that."

"Peacock and Updegraff fired the first shots. You going
to arrest them, and the bully-boys they had shooting at my
back?" Bat was breathing heavily. Deadly cool during the
battle, he was fighting hard to control his temper.

The Mayor lowered the shotgun. "Look, let's not have
any more trouble. Come along peaceable to the office and
pay your fine." He looked toward the calaboose where Peacock was supporting the wounded Updegraff. "You do that?"

"Would Updegraff have exposed himself to me unless he
knew I'd run out of lead?"

"Guess not," Webster allowed. "Comin' peaceable now?"

Bat nodded. The Mayor represented the law. Regardless of who had started the fight, Bat knew he was guilty of discharging a firearm within the city limits. He slapped the dust off his clothes.

The battle had lasted only a few minutes. When a long-legged fellow sprinted out of the Dodge House, half-dressed, trying to tuck in his shirttail, Bat demanded, "Where in blazes have you been?"

Jim's cheeks reddened. "I was sleeping until the gunfire broke out. What's going on here?"

"A fine thing! I come up from Tombstone to save your hide, and you don't even meet the train!"

Jim was astonished. "I didn't send out any call for help."

"Well, somebody did," Bat snapped, "and I dang near broke my neck getting here."

The Mayor fidgeted. "Do your talkin' later."

Bat and Jim followed him to the City Marshal's office.

"I guess you didn't know I'm not Marshal any more," Jim explained. "I resigned to keep an eye on the take at the dance hall."

"I appointed Fred Singer in Jim's place," the Mayor added.

Bat was boiling inside. He was furious at being sucked into a trap. A fine welcome from the town he had protected with his life! Fining him because he dared defend himself even before he'd had time to check his guns!

The police docket read, "W. B. Masterson did unlawfully and feloniously discharge a pistol on the streets. Fine, eight dollars. Paid."

As the two brothers walked back to the rooming house, Bat hauled out his watch. "The westbound train is due in less than three hours. Time enough to pack and dispose of your interest in the dance hall."

Taller than Bat, considered a colorless personality by those who had known the beloved Ed and the debonair Bat, Jim was also stubborn. "I'll leave when I'm good and ready."

Bat poured on the arguments until Jim said, "Oh, all right. Have it your way."

After checking Jim's gripsack at the station, Bat headed for Kelley's for steaks. Numerous friends were there, but Bat was hosting no celebration. He questioned all, "Who sent me that telegram?"

No one knew.

From Kelley's he and Jim marched to the dance hall. Peacock greeted them from a stool, a shotgun readied across his lap. Bat ignored it and began firing questions. "You send that telegram hauling me up from Tombstone?"

"No! You started this, Masterson, sending that fake message from Las Vegas."

"I sent no message."

"Yeah? Well, who did?"

The two glared at each other, then said simultaneously, "Hanged if I know!"

"Somebody wanted to pin my hide to the wall and, when I find out who it was, he'll wish he hadn't!" Bat remarked. Though Bat and others investigated further for weeks, the mystery was never solved.

Under Bat's stern eye Jim dissolved his partnership. Peacock paid off promptly. Then the two brothers went directly to the station.

"Mind if I ask where we're going?" Jim grumped.

"Pueblo. We can get a coach from there to Tombstone."

Jim took a deep breath. "I've heeled all I'm gonna. You go to Tombstone. I'm getting off at Trinidad."

"Why?"

"Because I was going to sell out anyway and move

there. I got an offer to be Deputy City Marshal there."

Bat slapped a bill in front of the ticket agent. "Two seats to Trinidad, Colorado."

He would give Trinidad a check; see what kind of situation Jim was getting. If it looked all right, then he would continue on to Arizona.

Bat took an immediate liking to Trinidad, a livestock and mining town near the Colorado–New Mexico boundary.

When Jim introduced his illustrious brother, the town leaders explained Trinidad was having its troubles with the lawless element. Cattle rustling was rampant. Cattlemen were importing gunmen to protect their herds. When sheepmen put their woollies on the free grass, the situation worsened. Recently prospectors had located iron, copper, and coal deposits nearby. "We have had no wild stampedes here. We don't want one, either."

"What do you want?" Bat asked pointedly.

Stop the shooting and rustling, and Trinidad could develop as a stockyards and smelter town.

"The right kind of Sheriff could settle this entire trouble inside a few months," Bat told them.

The Sheriff was afraid of his shadow. "We sure could use a bang-up deppity sheriff," the feed-store proprietor hinted strongly.

Bat said he appreciated their interest, but he must refuse. He had made big money in Ford County, Kansas. He had expensive tastes. He would consider only an offer permitting him to combine his activities of lawman and gambler.

"That's just what this town needs!" several agreed. A well-managed, respectable place where men could gather for a congenial evening free from gunfights and disreputable company. The businessmen excused themselves hastily. They would like to confer in private.

Bat grinned as the door closed behind them. "What do you think, Jim?"

If Jim resented the attention shown Bat, he didn't show it. But he did make one thing clear. "I can handle the Marshalship."

Bat was warming up to the idea of staying in Trinidad, if they made it worth his while. He detested Arizona. If Earp needed him, Bat could make the jump in good time.

Trinidad offered a real challenge. He would like to show Las Animas County how Bat Masterson handled rustlers, horse thieves, and such. He had chalked up a great reputation as a lawman. Why not keep at it? Also he could be near Jim.

When the businessmen filed back into the room, they offered Jim the Marshalship "at the salary and fees mentioned in our letter." Jim accepted.

They offered Bat one thousand dollars a month salary as Deputy Sheriff, mileage and bonus fees for arrests made. They would permit him to lease the gambling concession in the town's one establishment, "which will be enlarged and renovated."

Even by boom-town and top gunfighter standards, the offer was very generous. "How could I refuse, gentlemen?" Bat answered. Their appreciation of his talents was balm to his injured pride. "I'll give Las Animas full value," he promised.

There is no published account of Bat's activities in Trinidad. Old-timers claimed "he cut rustling to a nub." Jim left Trinidad some months later. Perhaps he did not want to work in the shadow of his famous brother. Bat was named his successor, so both town and county benefited from his guardianship.

Early in June, 1882, Wyatt Earp visited Bat briefly in Trinidad. The Tombstone troubles were over. On hearing the Gunnison mines were booming, he moved on to a new career as a free lance gambler.

Although Dodge was a sore spot, Bat returned there a year later when Luke Short hollered for help.

From Tombstone, Short invested his savings in Dodge's famous Long Branch saloon. Business was good, but no better than that of the establishments on either side: ex-Mayor George Hoover's liquor store and present Mayor A. B. "Ab" Webster's Alamo saloon. To draw a crowd Short imported a square grand piano and an attractive female pianist. Her crashing chords tolled the cowboys inside.

Hoover lost some trade, but Webster's Alamo was deserted. The louder the tinkling from the Long Branch, the less tinkling in his cash drawer. Too pinch-penny to hire a competing attraction, he figured how to put the skids under Short.

To assure his re-election Webster had campaigned on a "reform" ticket. A saloonkeeper heading a reform ticket would have been ridiculous anywhere but in Dodge. For years practically every city official and law officer had some connection with the liquor trade or gambling, still considered respectable enterprises.

Ab prevailed on the council to pass a city ordinance forbidding saloonkeepers to "provide entertainment on the violin, piano, or any other musical instrument." The noise "disturbed the peace around here," he claimed with tongue in cheek.

Luke Short promptly dismissed the pianist. That evening his customers trooped next door to the Alamo to hear his former pianist! As a gambler Luke was irked that the Mayor had run a bluff on him. As a businessman he resented the unfairness of music being unlawful in his place, and tolerated in defiance of the law in the Mayor's.

"I'll put gravel in Ab's grease," he muttered.

Two nights later the Long Branch had an orchestra

drowning out the Alamo's pianist. The cowboys were stacked thirty deep around his new attraction.

Webster fished another high card out of his sleeve. He sent two deputy marshals to arrest Short's musicians. The sawed-off gambler was out at the time. Hearing of this, he sought an officer to bail out his employees.

L. C. Hartman had been one of the deputies. When he saw Short approaching he fired his gun, and missed. Short returned the compliment, and missed. The next morning Short pleaded guilty to disturbing the peace, paid his fine, and started to leave. Instead, he found himself tossed into jail and held there until the eastbound Santa Fe was due. Under heavy armed guard the weaponless gambler was escorted to the station. "Get out of town, and stay out," he was told.

On arriving in Kansas City, Short telegraphed Bat he had been run out of Dodge unfairly, without being given a chance to recover his money. Bat caught the first train east and powwowed with Luke. Bat had no love for Webster. Ab had headed the ticket that defeated Bat, and had arrested Bat after the Battle of the Plaza. Now Webster had wronged a friend. "It's obvious he and his side-kicks are going to run Dodge to their advantage, and prevent competitors from exercising their rights as citizens." There was a wrong to right.

"Where do we start?" Luke asked.

After thinking it over, Bat made two swift moves. He telegraphed Wyatt Earp. Anticipating a showdown of the Tombstone variety, Earp recruited four scrappers: Texas Jack Vermilion, Dan Tipton, Johnny Millsap, and Johnny Green. They headed for Dodge.

Then Bat called Governor George W. Glick and explained the situation. The Governor agreed Short had been treated badly. He knew Bat by reputation. "What do you plan to do?"

"All I ask, Mr. Governor, is that Short and I be allowed to re-establish ourselves if we can; and that if those crooks in Dodge yell for the militia, you won't send them to aid Webster and his bunch."

The Governor had visions of gun-smoked streets and bodies lying in windrows. "All right. Re-establish yourselves if you can. If Webster calls for the militia, I'll send a negotiator instead."

"Thank you, sir." Bat hung up and whooped. "Now back to Dodge!"

But Earp and his boys got to Dodge first. Deputy City Marshal Prairie Dog Dave Morrow happened to be at the station. One look at the artillery and he reminded them that wearing firearms inside the city limits was prohibited.

Earp stroked his fulsome mustache. "Well now, Dave, we came to see justice done. The way we see it, we're representing law and order. Luke Short has been cheated. We're here to protect his rights as a citizen. Seems like we ought to get deputized, so we can keep our guns."

Morrow swallowed hard. "You're mighty persuasive," he told Earp, smiling nervously. But he deputized the five.

Earp and Company then headed across Front Street, with Earp sending the four "deputies" to cover the Plaza. Mayor Webster blustered out of the Alamo. "Looky here, Earp, we don't aim to have no trouble around here."

The towering ex-Marshal answered softly, "Not anticipating trouble, Mayor. Just waiting for Bat and Luke."

Webster blanched and dived back into the saloon. County Attorney Mike Sutton was at the bar. "Call out the militia!" Ab demanded.

Sutton slipped out the back way, and called the Governor. Then he dragged back to the Alamo. "No dice. The Governor is sending the Adjutant General to negotiate." The two kept each other company until they saw Bat and Luke step off the westbound train. Sutton ducked out, grabbed a horse, and raced eastward. As the Ford County *Globe* reported, "On the return of Luke Short and his friends it didn't take Mike Sutton long to arrive at the conclusion that Kinsley was a much healthier locality, and that is now his abiding place."

Adjutant General Colonel Thomas Moonlight arrived by special train and called a meeting. Earp stated his opinion emphatically: "If Ab Webster can have a piano player, Luke Short can have one. If Luke can't have one, no one else can."

"We're here to see Luke gets an even break. We can stay indefinitely," Bat stated.

Colonel Moonlight looked at the Mayor and his Councilmen. "Mr. Short has been deprived of his constitutional rights. Well, gentlemen?"

The Councilmen put their heads together briefly, then a spokesman said, "We hereby rescind the ordinance prohibiting musical entertainment."

"What good will that do?" Short appealed to the Colonel. "Bat and Wyatt won't be five miles out of town before I'll be havin' trouble again."

"Very well," Moonlight decided, "I will appoint a Peace Commission to assure that your rights as a citizen are protected. The Commission will remain here until I am assured there will be no such further trouble to you, or anyone else." The Colonel looked around the crowded room. "As members of the Peace Commission I will appoint you, Luke; Wyatt Earp, Bat Masterson, Charlie Bassett . . . and Neal Brown, Bill Harris, Frank McLane, and Billy Potillion. I myself will be chairman. Meeting adjourned, gentlemen."

The Websterites knew they were whipped. With the exception of the chairman, the Commission was anything but peaceful in character. The members were all top gunfighters, and long-time friends.

While the Mayor and his supporters slumped out, the *Globe* reporter suggested the Commission have its picture taken.

The members trooped to the photographic gallery. They brushed their suits, combed their locks, smoothed their sweeping mustaches, and wiped their boots. Five sat stiffly on a bench; four stood behind with shoulders squared. All looked grim and purposeful.

Decades later this would be one of the most famous prints of the great gunfighters of the West.

The Peace Commission played poker and swapped shop-talk over rare steaks. The *Globe* reported: "Our city trouble is about over and things in general will be conducted as of old. A new dance house was opened Saturday night where all the warriors met and settled their past differences and everything was made lovely and serene. All opposing factions met and agreed to stand by each other for the good of the trade. A not unlooked-for result. Luke Short . . . we believe, has come to stay."

In that last statement the *Globe* erred. Luke sold out and moved to Texas. The others scattered. But Bat had decided somebody had to keep the law upright in the saddle. For months he kept an eagle eye on his multiple responsibilities at Trinidad, and still managed to drop into Dodge now and then.

When Webster filed for re-election, Bat wrote letters concerning his qualifications to the *Globe*. Always forthright in expressing himself, he used language even the *Globe* would not publish.

Once more Webster favored a reform platform, and with good reason. The Santa Fe Railroad was now under the management of proper Bostonians. On inspection tours they had spent a night or two in their private cars on the siding at Dodge. The Easterners' ears were offended by the cowboys howling it up on Front Street and across the Deadline.

Mayor Webster was told that either Dodge presented one-way tickets out of town to the disreputable element or the railroad would not invest money in a roundhouse, enlarged livestock pens, more sidings, even a hospital. They would choose some other town as a major point in their system.

The townspeople listened when Candidate Webster told them, "The Santa Fe made this town. It can break it. If the management says gambling and dance halls got to go, I'll see that they do. Let's make a solid, respectable town out of Dodge."

Hearing that Webster had slandered the respectable profession of gambling and was bound to be a shoo-in, Bat decided the campaign needed his personal attention. He took a brief leave of absence from Trinidad, and arrived in Dodge late in October, 1884.

Even Dodge was not prepared for his latest maneuver. Bat announced, "I am establishing a newspaper to inform the good people of the truth of the situation around here, and the hypocrisies of certain undesirables who mean to keep feeding at the public trough." Bat well knew the influence a newspaper had in elections. If the *Globe* failed to serve the best interests of the people by not printing his letters, he would publish them himself!

The editor of the long-established, popular *Globe* was amused rather than worried. "What will you call your publication?"

"*Vox Populi* . . . Voice of the People," Bat answered with supreme confidence. Within a few days the new press and professional staff would arrive.

This was the heyday of name-calling, with no journalistic holds barred, and none fearing libel suits. Bat went all out.

Decades later Bat insisted the *Vox Populi* defeated Webster and his slate. He inferred numerous issues were printed.

Historians claim only one issue came off the press. Of its debut the *Globe* commented, "The howling over that issue still goes on."

The Trinidad (Colorado) *News* reported loyally, "Bat is an easy and graceful writer and possesses real journalistic ability. The *News* will be glad to hear of his making a howling success."

George G. Thompson, an outstanding researcher on Bat Masterson, wrote, "The paper did not survive its first edition; but the editor did, which was more than some people expected, considering the things Bat printed concerning his political opponents."

But Dodgeites held short grudges. In a contest sponsored as part of the 1885 Fourth of July celebration to choose "the most popular man in Dodge," the winner was William Barclay Masterson. For many years Bat carried the gold-headed cane presented him for having won that honor.

15. A SIEGE AT CIMARRON

Of the years 1885 to 1902 Bat Masterson wrote later, "I made Denver my home base. I was in and out every few months, traveling mostly around the west. But I always ended up back in Denver."

When Trinidad became too quiet, thanks to Bat's efforts, he turned in his badge. Wide-open Denver beckoned with its lure of excitement and big money. Barely settled in a plush boardinghouse, Bat was offered a post as a deputy sheriff for Arapahoe County, of which Denver was the county seat.

Shortly after, he resigned in disgust. "There isn't an honest man on this force! I was hired to enforce the law, not corrupt it. When I arrest a man I don't expect to see him go scot-free after paying bribe money. I never lived off graft. I don't intend to start now. Goodbye!" He slapped on the derby and stomped out.

He headed straight for the Arcade. A long-established gamblinghouse, the Arcade had a widespread reputation for being absolutely aboveboard. Big-time gamblers from all over the country visited there periodically. Those who dealt poker or faro for a percentage of the winnings, or conducted other games of chance, such as roulette, Twenty-One, Over and Under Seven, Lasconeete or Chinese Lottery, had to be the best in the business: gentlemanly, quick-witted, masters of game psychology, and scrupulously trust-worthy.

The management welcomed the illustrious Masterson to its payroll. Patrons flocked to his table. None ever expressed dissatisfaction with his conduct of the game and he pros-pered. He indulged in pastel-colored suits, fancy shirts and waistcoats, diamond rings, jeweled studs and cuff links. Even while playing cards Bat sported a derby hat. It be-came his trademark.

Free from bracing himself against towering Texans, or walking in the shadow of the tall Wyatt Earp, Bat stopped wearing high-heeled boots, or shoes with built-up heels. He was still flat-stomached and walked erect. He preferred the company of men. His favorite recreation was attending prize fights.

Here he was more than a spectator. He increased his al-ready expert knowledge of the sport. He studied the styles and careers of the coming and the established boxers. Sports writers sought his opinions and quoted him freely.

Let there be one low blow or evidence of dishonest refereeing, and the voice heard loudest was Bat Master-son's. "I love the game. By Godfrey, it's going to stay on the up-and-up if I personally have to buffalo every tinhorn who tries to put his dirty hands on it to make a killing in dishonest betting!"

Now and then Bat appeared in one of Denver's plushy restaurants or theaters with a beautiful girl on his arm. He was courtly, always the gentleman; his private life was exactly that, private, and completely free of scandal. He had yet to meet the girl he wanted to marry, and he cher-ished his freedom.

Bat needed absolute liberty of movement. On a moment's notice he would hop on a train, traveling to some distant city to attend a championship boxing match.

In the fall of 1885 at Rawlins, Wyoming, Bat served as the "third man in the ring," the umpire at the Clow–Hands fight. The match was a big one. Special trains brought fans and gamblers from all over the country. In a detailed account of the fight, which Clow won in the sixth round, the *Rocky Mountain News* stated, "Masterson makes a ready umpire."

Returning to Denver, Bat switched from the Arcade to the Palace on Blake Street. He knew, as did thousands, that Denver was one of the most corrupt cities in the country. The police force was rotten to the core. Dishonest city and county officials fattened on payoff moneys. Lou Blonger controlled a dime lottery racket nationwide in scope, as well as local bunko and confidence games. Denver had crooked gamblers by the score, but none dared set foot in the Arcade, the Palace, or the Central.

The Palace was housed in an ornate two-story brick structure with a variety theater on the first floor and gambling rooms upstairs. Having acquired a taste for vaudeville in Dodge City, Bat often dropped in to catch the new acts.

He was happy, famous, respected, popular, and very prosperous. He felt he had hung up his guns for good. Then a new kind of lawlessness flared hotly in Kansas.

In the late eighteen-eighties the sparsely settled extreme western part of Kansas broke out in a rash of new towns. Unscrupulous promoters would purchase a quarter-section of land for three hundred dollars from the United States Land Office, and subdivide it into town lots. Lured by dishonest promises, gullible people bought the lots. The promoters pocketed one-hundred-thousand-dollar profits and skipped out.

Often the new communities were neighbor to established ones. Soon all became embroiled in contests to decide which would be chosen as the county seat, the only chance for economic survival. The contests developed into bloody feuds. At first, voters were intimidated and ballot boxes stuffed. Next, gunmen were hired to steal county records and county seals without which no documents were legal. In several instances even the clapboard courthouses were kidnapped and removed to the rival location!

When Leoti and Coronado fought to be county seat of Wichita County, Leotians imported two notorious killers, Charles Coulter and William Rains. The gun battle at the polls ended with the two killers and one Coronadoan killed, and four others gravely wounded. Leoti won.

Bat first entered the picture when an eccentric eastern millionaire "adopted" the fledgling community of Ingalls, in Gray County, and determined to make it "overnight into another Kansas City." Asa Soule, manufacturer of Hop Bitters, bought much real estate in Ingalls, imported workers to build a ninety-mile irrigating canal and a sorghum-cane processing plant. He promised that if Ingalls were chosen county seat over Cimarron, the temporary one, he would build a branch railroad and found a college.

The election was set at a neutral location between the two towns. Soule offered Bat a thousand dollars to insure "Ingalls' best interests." Bat was only too glad to serve on behalf of an unhampered election. He took the train to Dodge, and there enlisted Bill Tilghman, Ben Daniels, Eat-'Em-Up Jake, and the Gilbert brothers to assist him. The voting was orderly, and Ingalls won. Bat collected the thousand dollars, divvied up with his friends, and returned to Denver.

But Cimarron petitioned the Supreme Court to declare the election null and void, claiming the overanxious Soule had imported unqualified voters.

Ingalls charged Cimarron promised to pay members of the Foote Township Equalization Society ten thousand dollars to vote for Cimarron.

Months passed in bitter litigation. Once more Ingalls won, the Supreme Court holding "there was a *little* more fraud committed by Cimarron than Ingalls."

A delegation from Ingalls called at Cimarron to receive the county records and seal. They were run out of town.

"Send for Masterson!" Soule roared. "He'll get 'em!"

Once more Bat detrained at Dodge, and found Soule had already provided him with a choice small army: Bill Tilghman, Jim Marshall, Ed Brooks, Billy Ainsworth, George Bolds, Neal Brown, Fred Singer, Newt Watson, and Charlie Reicheldeffer.

Bat stood for drinks and steaks at Kelley's, and planned the action. "Tomorrow is Sunday. If we ride into Cimarron quietly, we can get those records and be out of there before the town wakes up."

Very early the morning of January 12, 1889, the Masterson party rolled into Cimarron. They rode in a spring wagon in which they expected to carry away the records and other paraphernalia. All men were braced with six-guns and cartridge belts. A few had rifles. "Marshall and I will enter first," Bat said. "The records are in a room on the second floor. We'll toss them out the window. The rest of you cover us, and keep anyone from interfering. Ready?"

The men nodded.

Bat and Jim Marshall, a veteran peace officer who sported a white goatee, slipped through the front door. In the first office they were surprised to find County Clerk A. T. Riley working on his books. One look at their drawn guns, and Riley was "disinclined to argue." They tied him up and tossed his ledgers through the window.

On the second floor the two scooped up armloads of books and hurried back to the wagon. "Here's the official seal,"

Bat explained, placing it in the wagon. "Some of you give us a hand."

Bolds was just leaving the courthouse, arms loaded, when buckshot raked the doorway. He tossed the books into the wagon, drew his gun, and fired at a man shooting at him from a rooftop across the street.

Suddenly bullets and shotgun pellets poured from doorways, street corners, and other rooftops.

"We've got to get out of here!" Tilghman shouted, trying to control the frightened team with his left hand and fire a six-gun with his right.

Bolds ducked inside and shouted, "Everybody out. We're leaving!"

Bat leaped to the stairway. "Keep us covered three minutes and we'll have the place cleaned out."

Bolds, Brown, Ainsworth, and Watson blasted through the doorway, guns spitting. Tilghman shoved the reins at Reicheldeffer. "Start pulling out. We'll cover you."

Reicheldeffer and four others leaped onto the wagon just as a bullet creased one of the horses. It bolted, dragging its teammate. The driver toppled back, a bullet through his hip. Nevertheless, he grabbed the reins and fought to slow the team. Meanwhile Bat and Jim Marshall were firing from the second-floor window to help cover Tilghman and the others caught afoot. At the far end of the street he figured some sixty horsemen were milling around, waiting to charge the courthouse.

Bolds saw them too, and dropped one rider.

"Don't shoot to kill. Hit their horses," Bat shouted from above.

"Here they come!"

But the charge disintegrated as wounded horses reared and screamed.

"Pull back to the gully," Tilghman ordered the men

alongside him; and they raced off, leaving Bat and Marshall in the building.

The courthouse was already surrounded. Bat stayed at the window and Marshall covered the stairway from behind a barricade of tables and chairs.

"Surrender, or we'll dynamite the building!" men roared from outside.

Bat shouted, "We're officers of the law. We don't want to kill anybody. You're preventing us from doing our duty. We'll kill whoever tries to enter to dynamite this place."

The battle in the streets had lasted less than fifteen minutes. The siege of the courthouse strung out over thirty hours!

Bat and Marshall held off the crowd throughout the long sunny day. As dusk closed in and the mercury dropped, a good many left. Those determined to see the fight to a finish took turns firing from doorways, and ducking inside to warm up and gulp coffee.

The two lawmen stamped their feet and blew on their fingers. Bat kept one hand, and then the other, tucked under an armpit so his fingers wouldn't stiffen.

In the morning Jake Shoup, one of the Cimarron officials, ordered Bat to surrender.

Without exposing himself Bat hollered, "Surrender! And have you string us up? We've got plenty of ammunition left. We can hold out until Tilghman gets back with reinforcements."

That possibility cooled more heads than the chilly weather. Finally Shoup called out, "All right, we'll make a deal. Stop firing, and I and my friends will provide you safe escort to the railroad station."

"We won't give up our guns," Bat answered, sure Shoup meant to trap him and Marshall.

"Word of honor. Keep your guns. There's been enough blood spilled."

Bat's face was blackened with powder smoke. His coat and trousers were dirty. But the derby was as cock-angled as ever as he emerged with Marshall, and his eyes the color of river ice.

As they walked stiff-backed to the station, Bat looked around. Not a window whole. Good horses dead. Surely some Cimarron men dead or wounded. And all because some slicksters promoted a new town, and Asa Soule had empire-building on the brain. Cimarron should have accepted the Supreme Court decision, but hadn't. "All this for dirty county records!" Bat muttered under his breath. Everybody evading the law, and shooting at the lawmen.

The siege at Cimarron was the last of the county-seat battles. Crippling blizzards and prolonged drought discouraged new settlements. Kansas had to dig in to survive a severe economic depression. When prosperity finally returned, the heyday of the town promoter was over. And so was that of the gunfighter. The frontiering was over.

Bat resumed dealing at the Palace.

Early in 1891 Ed Chase, the owner, suggested, "Since Ed Gaylord got married, his wife won't let him manage the theater downstairs. Want to try your hand at it? I'll make it worth your while."

Bat laughed. "Manage a theater where the most celebrated entertainers and beautiful showgirls play? You bet!"

His job included maintaining order backstage and out front, and providing a topnotch program. Because he was popular, full of quips and jokes and "could charm the eyelashes off a buzzard," Bat did well.

In the fall, new attractions from the East joined the troupe. Among them were the famous Barbour sisters, Frances and Addie, and Emma Walters. Bat found his attention drawn to the lovely blonde Emma. "Now there's a girl with fourteen-karat class!" He sent her flowers and

candy, and took her out to dinner. But he had always done
that to pretty girls, and as regularly lost interest when they
turned bossy, or unladylike or mercenary.

Emma was different: good company, a superb listener,
refined without being stuffy. No doubt about it, she was
crazy about Bat. Their courtship flourished. It dawned on
Bat that he was falling in love. "Oh no!" He couldn't give
up his freedom. He couldn't face regular hours, and account-
ing to someone for his varied activities.

One evening, however, he blurted, "I'm terribly in love
with you, Emma. I want to marry you. But I can't! I mean,
don't let me. I'd make you miserable. I'd be the worst hus-
band in the world."

Emma slipped her arms around his neck. "I'm in love
with you, Bat. But I've been a showgirl too long to be like
most wives. I can't cook. I don't want a rose-covered cottage.
I'm used to breakfasting at noon. I like late hours, and
getting all dressed up to go out to dinner. I like your kind of
people . . . but, most of all, I love you.· I know I can make
you happy."

"Marriage is for keeps, Emma," Bat added.

"For always," she murmured, kissing him.

On November 21, 1891, three days before his thirty-
eighth birthday, William Barclay Masterson and Emma
Walters were married in a civil ceremony. Ed Chase and his
wife, the former Frances Barbour, were the only attendants.
For this solemn occasion Bat and Emma wanted privacy.

It didn't take Bat long to realize that in Emma he had
found a wonderful wife. She gladly gave up her career and
accepted his way of life, the ups and downs inescapable
in marriage to a gambling man. They remained wholly
devoted to each other to the day of Bat's death.

Very early in 1892 bonanza silver deposits were located
in the mountains nearby. Almost overnight a town of ten
thousand, named Creede for its discoverer, burgeoned on

the slopes. Thirty saloons and gamblinghouses operated around the clock. The Denver firm of Watrous, Banninger and Company offered Bat a large salary to manage their establishment. By "manage" they meant keep order, and make a good profit.

In February, Bat and Emma moved to Creede. Bat reported for work wearing a lavender corduroy suit, black tie, and black bowler hat. His hair was graying at the temples and thinning on top. His eyes were as flinty as ever when need be. Other places knew brawling and gunfights. While Bat was on the floor the Watrous, Banninger place had no trouble.

Before the year was out, the boom was over. Bat and Emma returned to Denver, Bat to deal at the Palace. He scarcely knew when, but one by one the honest places were taken over by a powerful element, forerunner of the modern-day racketeering gangs. This condition was fostered by corrupt law officers and city officials who wanted more and more payoff money to split among themselves.

All gamblers were required to pay protection fees. "Never!" Bat snapped.

The police chief sent two men to bring Bat in "for questioning."

Bat chased them out into the street. Then the chief himself, resplendent in blue serge and gold buttons, broke up Bat's game. "Who do you think you are, Masterson? Just because you slapped a gun off cowboys' heads in a little burg like Dodge City doesn't mean you're going to push my men around. You're under arrest for interfering with the due process of law!"

Bat shot to his feet. "Why, you bulb-nosed, bleary-eyed chaw, you pork-livered pig, before I'll help fatten your pocket and that of every tinhorn, two-faced double-dealing grayback, I'll quit! And as for arresting me—" He twisted the chief's nose between his thumb and fingers and hauled the bellowing man out in the street. "You've got plenty of lice to feed on! Leave honest gambling men alone!"

From that time until he left Denver in 1902 Bat worked for no gamblinghouse in Denver. He continued to play poker as a private individual, and won more often than lost. He and Emma traveled a good deal, and everywhere Bat was recognized as a skillful, honest man at cards.

The one thing that drew him back to Denver time and time again was prize fighting. Denver was the boxing capital of the world then. He loved everything about the sport.

On March 17, 1897, Bat was in charge of the large squad of police imported to prevent a riot when Gentleman Jim Corbett fought Bob Fitzsimmons for the heavyweight championship at Carson City, Nevada.

On April 9, 1899, he was chosen official referee for the Colorado Athletic Association. When the founders quarreled, Bat resigned and formed his own Olympic Athletic Club. For two years he refereed the main bouts, recruited boxers, and kept the two-thousand-seat arena at Sixteenth and Market streets operating at a profit.

But so lucrative a business drew competitors. Bat incurred losses which he paid out of his own pocket. Before long the curtain came down on the golden days of Denver pugilism.

"Well, that's that," Bat summed it up for Emma. "I've paid every bill. I'm busted. Flat broke."

Emma stroked the bald place on the top of his head, ran a finger lightly over the short-clipped gray mustache. "You'll find something else. With all the friends you have, something will turn up."

Bat's shoulders sagged against the chair. "I'm forty-six, Emma. I'm not trained to be anything but a gunfighter, or a gambler, or a boxing promoter." He looked sad. "I never thought I'd see the day when I was outdated!"

"I don't believe it. Something will turn up. Just be patient."

Men who were friends of both President Theodore Roosevelt and Bat knew that the President was an avid fan of anything Western: stories, adventures, gunfighters, cattlemen. They wrote him, recalling Bat's fine years as a lawman at Dodge, and expressed the hope a Marshalship might be available to a man who had done so much to bring order to the frontier. Through an aide, President Roosevelt offered Bat the position of United States Marshal in charge of Oklahoma.

Perhaps Bat's discouragement went deeper than even Emma realized. Perhaps it was based on a bone-deep weariness, the result of living hard and fast, of living up to his own reputation. Some or all of this figured in his turning down the offer.

Bat wrote "T. R." in his colorful style: "I am not the man for the job. Oklahoma is still woolly, and if I were marshal, some youngster would want to try me out on account of my reputation. I would be a bait for grown-up kids who had fed on dime novels. I would have to kill, or be killed. No sense to that. I have taken my guns off, and I don't ever want to put them on again."

Emma had saved a little money. "You need a change. Go have yourself a time in St. Louis, or wherever you want. You'll come back feeling like a new man."

Bat was gone for weeks. He returned looking much older and disillusioned. "Looks like Lady Luck has deserted me."

He kept playing in private games, winning some, losing a lot. He pawned his and Emma's jewels. He began drinking heavily. Never quarrelsome, he became involved in ugly arguments. He brooded over the evil that controlled Denver. One night he strapped on his guns and, in a drunken stupor, set out to clean up Denver.

Word reached District Attorney Harry Lindsley that Bat

was on a rampage, drunk, armed, and dangerous. "I ought to arrest him, but he won't stand for it without a fight. He'll put up a fight and some of my boys will go under. I wish some of Bat's old friends were in town. They'd know how to handle him."

But who was there? Earp was in Alaska, Luke Short in Texas, Tilghman in Oklahoma. . . . Suddenly Lindsley remembered Jim Marshall, now Cripple Creek's lawman. He picked up the telephone and summoned white-goateed Marshall to Denver.

"I'll report in tomorrow morning," Marshall promised.

It didn't take long for Bat to hear the man who had withstood the siege of Cimarron was coming to Denver to disarm him. He reeled out to the nearest telegraph office and wired Marshall, "Will be waiting for you at barbershop near Tabor Opera House between ten and eleven tomorrow morning."

He spent the night drinking in a saloon. But his inner raging at defeat, at humiliation, at a changing world where there was no place for a man of his outdated talents, must have burned off the deadening effects of the alcohol.

Shortly before ten in the morning he hauled out the six-gun that had seen so much action in Dodge, checked the chambers, and holstered it again. The clear, cold gray eyes of the younger gunfighter were now bloodshot. His supple fingers waggled like rubber bands. His suit was wrinkled and speckled with cigar ashes; his once firm cheeks sagged with a suspicion of jowls. Only the bowler hat remained dapper and defiant as Bat stamped along to the showdown.

He perched on a stool in full view of the door, ignoring the immediate rush of patrons and barbers out the back. He waited . . . and waited . . . The longer he waited, the more his anger cooled. Come right down to it, he couldn't raise a gun against a fellow lawman. He was relieved when the hour slipped by and Marshall had not appeared.

"Gotta have a drink," he mumbled, staggering to the bar at the Tabor House. He was lifting the glass to his mouth when he felt a gentle prod in his back. He looked up into the mirror. Jim Marshall had the drop on him.

"You're going to kill me, Jim?"

"Not if you're reasonable, Bat."

"What do you mean 'reasonable'?"

"Times have changed, old boy. You can't hurrah Denver. It's too big." Marshall cleared his throat. The words were coming hard. "Thirty years ago I would have told you to ride out of town—"

"No!" Bat flared. "Thirty years ago no man, not even you, ever got the drop on me!"

Marshall nodded. "You missed the point. I do have the drop on you. And I—I'm telling you you're on your way out of town."

Bat paled. Of all the great humiliations, being run out of town was the worst. He shook his head as if to deny the fact that he must go. "I'll need a little time. Have to pack . . . tell Emma . . ."

The pressure of the gun increased a little. "Take the four-o'clock Burlington, Bat."

"You're not even giving me twenty-four hours."

"Don't press me," Marshall cried out. "Can't you see I'm trying to keep you from being killed! Will you do as I say, and take the four-o'clock Burlington?"

Bat's head sunk on his chest. After a bit he rallied, tried to shrug in the old devil-may-care way, and almost toppled over. Then he shuffled off to the apartment.

"I'll send for you as soon as possible," he promised Emma.

Bat took the four-o'clock eastbound Burlington. Not a soul was at the station to say goodbye.

16.
MASTERSON'S VIEWS ON TIMELY TOPICS

———————

BAT ARRIVED IN NEW YORK CITY SOBER AND SORRY. HE WAS determined to wipe the tarnish off his reputation. But good intentions were not enough. He had to find a job, and soon.

He had chosen New York City not only because it was a long way from Denver. It was celebrity-heaven. The town had never entertained a famous, fearless top-drawer gun-fighter. But Easterners knew much fiction and some truth about Earp, Masterson, Hickok, Tom Smith, Bill Tilghman, and others because their newspapers for years had sent their top feature writers West to interview these luminaries.

Bat figured that since he was a celebrity New York would welcome him with open arms. He wouldn't be mewing for a job. The offers would come to him.

When he stepped off the train, he was all set for the lime-light. The porter had brushed and pressed his suit. His cheeks were close-shaven and pink from applications of hot towels and scented lotion. He still sported a gold chain and jeweled fob across a creamy satin vest. His suit coat was

nervous. "Hobnobbing with Presidents isn't exactly my line," he told Emma.

Her cheeks glowing, Emma packed his bag and sent him off to Washington.

When Bat stepped across the threshold of the White House, he took off his derby. He sat quietly in a row of chairs filled with important politicians, statesmen, and officials waiting to see "T. R." He was surprised to hear his name called before many others. When the receptionist opened the door to the President's office, a big voice boomed out, "Hello, Bat Masterson. Glad to see you. Sit down. Sit down."

For nearly an hour the great Teddy fired questions at Bat. He knew considerable about the Old West and also about championship boxing. Problems, crises—all were pushed into the background as the two chatted. "Come and see me again," President Roosevelt urged when it was time for Bat to leave.

For several years thereafter Theodore Roosevelt and William Barclay Masterson enjoyed further talks.

In 1907 William E. Lewis, a newspaperman, offered Bat a job on the New York *Morning Telegraph*. Lewis had interviewed Bat at Trinidad, Creede, and Denver while doing a feature series on famous frontiersmen.

"Doing what?" Bat asked "W.E.," as Lewis was called. They were talking over a friendly glass at Shanley's.

"Sports editor."

Bat's eyes glowed. Here was a rare-beefsteak-and-pepper-sass kind of job! His flanks were getting flabby riding a desk chair. "You really think I could do it?"

Lewis nodded.

Bat brushed his finger across his white clipped mustache. He was almost fifty-four, pretty old to tackle a new profession. Of course, writing wasn't exactly new to him. For over thirty years he had been firing off letters to editors, or being interviewed about the West or boxing. Through friends, he had been invited to do a series of authentic articles on Wyatt Earp and other famous gunfighters for the magazine *Human Life*. The editor was very enthusiastic about the features already finished.

"I'd have to write as I see things," Bat warned W.E.

"That's exactly what I want—the personal viewpoint."

The *Morning Telegraph* was Bat's kind of paper, specializing in sports news, theatrical and racing news. Racy, but colorful reading; anything but stuffy. The offices were in a remodeled car barn at Eighth Avenue and West Fiftieth. "Would I have to punch a time clock?"

"No. Do the job your way. Just have your daily column on the spindle by two P.M."

Never modest but long removed from youthful bragging, Bat knew he was the man for the job. Afternoons and evenings he would mingle with boxers, managers, promoters, and trainers. During the season he would attend the horse races on Long Island. He resigned the Marshalship. During the next fourteen years Bat Masterson wrote "Masterson's Views on Timely Topics." In subject matter and style he was judged the equal of his associates: Irvin S. Cobb, Frank O'Malley, even Richard Harding Davis.

Cobb described Bat thus: "Two things betokened the real man: his eyes. They were smoothed ovals of gray schist with flecks of mica glittering in them if he was aroused. But you might not notice the glint in those eyes unless you looked closely—it came and was instantly gone. And some of the men who faced him through the smoke fogs of cowtown melees hadn't lived long enough to get a good look."

Bat remained a celebrity among celebrities. His accomplishments brought lasting luster to his reputation. Though Emma was not seen too frequently on his night sojourns, friends admitted they were a devoted couple. In his column Bat hit hard when he suspected underhandedness or illegal practices in boxing or any other sport. He knew the soapy-eared newcomers and the bruised champions. To his final column Bat fought for the right side and honest conduct whether it be in boxing, racing, or everyday living.

As Damon Runyon later wrote of Bat, "He gained a wide reputation for his fearless writing. Four square to all the winds that blew, he despised hypocrisy and dishonesty, and he had a forceful way of expressing his feelings."

His was a familiar face at ringside and horse races; at Jack Dunston's restaurant, the Metropole, Doyle's Billiard Academy, and the bars at the Hoffman House, the Knickerbocker Hotel, and Rector's.

Now and then a stranger would ask "to see the gun that killed twenty-six men." Bat would arrange a meeting for the next day. Then he would go to a pawnshop, purchase a secondhand Colt .45, dig some notches in the butt, and show it to the stranger. Invariably the man would offer an extravagant price for the gun, and Bat, owl-eyed with repressed mirth, would pocket the money. Occasionally it rankled him that others could be so stupid as to think a man would brag up one killing, let alone the twenty or more attributed to Bat. He was a legend now. Even feature writers who knew Bat had killed his older brother's two murderers and the brawling Sergeant King refused to hold to the facts. They, too, prescribed to the "twenty or more notches" fiction.

The years rolled by. In the spring of 1921, when he was sixty-seven years old, an earnest young woman reporter on the *Morning Telegraph* sought his advice. "Should I bet fifty dollars on Jess Willard, the defending heavyweight champion, or this new challenger, Jack Dempsey?"

"Bet on Willard," the old expert told Louella Parsons.

"But I dreamed Dempsey beat Willard," she protested.

"Dempsey hasn't got a chance."

"Well, you ought to know." Louella plunged her savings on Willard.

Dempsey landed a punch that knocked Willard off the championship throne. Louella Parsons wrote later, "For days the big bold sheriff of Dodge City wouldn't look me in the eye without cringing." Then she added, "He was just a kindhearted old man."

Maybe so, but Bat was still punching out a forceful column. He thought little of a much-ballyhooed match between Lew Tendler, the Philadelphia southpaw, and Rocky Kansas of Buffalo. Midday of October 25 Bat went to the office to write up his views on the fight:

"Lew Tendler received a little more than $12,000 for his scrap with Rocky Kansas. Not so bad for a little job like that, and by the way, Rocky got nearly $10,000 for the part he played in the show. No wonder these birds are flying high when they can get that sort of money for an hour's work. Just think of an honest, hard-working farmer laboring from daylight to dark for forty of the best years of his life, and lucky if he finishes with as much as one of those birds gets in an hour. Yet there are those who argue that everything breaks even in this old dump of a world of ours.

"I suppose these ginks who argue that way hold that because the rich man gets ice in the summer and the poor man gets it in the winter, things are breaking even for both. Maybe so, but I can't see it that way."

Suddenly his fingers dug into the copy paper. The man who had written of countless knockouts slumped at his desk.

A little later a reporter found him. "I thought the old boy had fallen asleep. I didn't realize he had gone down for the long count."

Over five hundred attended the funeral service conducted by the Reverend Nathan Seagle, pastor of St. Stephen's

Episcopal Church. Active and honorary pallbearers made up a roster of men famous in journalism and sports. Burial was in Woodlawn Cemetery.

In the New York *American*, Damon Runyon wrote, "His death was a strangely quiet closing to a strangely active career. He was a 100 percent, 22-karat real man. . . . Bat was a good hater and a wonderful friend. He was always stretching out a helping hand to some down-and-outer. He had a great sense of humor and a marvelous fund of reminiscence, and was one of the most entertaining companions we have ever known. There are only too few men in the world like Bat Masterson, and his death is a genuine loss."

BIBLIOGRAPHY

Bradley, Glenn Danford. *The Story of the Santa Fe.* Boston: R. G. Badger, 1920

Coolidge, Dane. *Fighting Men of the West.* New York: E. P. Dutton & Co., 1932

Crawford, Samuel. *Kansas in the Sixties.* Chicago: A. C. McClurg & Co., 1911

Crumbine, Samuel. *Frontier Doctor.* Philadelphia: Dorrance, 1948

Davis, Clyde Brion. *The Arkansas.* New York: Farrar & Rinehart, 1940

Dixon, Olive. *The Life of Billy Dixon.* Dallas: P. L. Turner Co., 1940

Foy, Eddie and Harlow, Alvin. *Clowning Through Life.* New York: E. P. Dutton & Co., 1928

Harris, Foster. *The Look of the Old West.* New York: Viking Press, Inc., 1956

Haven, Charles and Belden, Frank. *A History of the Colt Revolver.* New York: William Morrow & Co., 1940

Horan, James. *Across the Cimarron.* New York: Crown Publishers, 1956

Hough, Emerson. *The Story of the Outlaw.* New York: Grosset & Dunlap, 1907

Lake, Stuart. *Wyatt Earp, Frontier Marshal.* Boston: Houghton Mifflin Co., 1931

Lardner, John. *White Hopes and Other Tigers.* Philadelphia: J. B. Lippincott Co., 1951

Monaghan, Jay. *The Great Rascal.* Boston: Little, Brown and Co., 1952

Myers, John Myers. *Doc Holliday.* Boston: Little, Brown and Co., 1955

O'Connor, Richard. *Bat Masterson.* New York: Doubleday & Co., 1957

Parsons, John. *The Peacemaker and Its Rivals, an Account of the Single Action Colt.* New York: William Morrow & Co., 1950

Parsons, Louella. *The Gay Illiterate.* New York: Doubleday, Doran & Co., Inc., 1944

Raine, William McLeod. *Famous Sheriffs and Western Outlaws.* Garden City: Doubleday, Doran, 1929

————. *Guns of the Frontier.* Boston: Houghton Mifflin Co., 1940

Sandoz, Mari. *The Buffalo Hunters.* New York: Hastings House, 1954

Shirley, Glenn. *Six Gun and Silver Star.* Albuquerque: University of New Mexico Press, 1955

Smith, Winston. *The Sharps Rifle.* New York: William Morrow & Co., 1943

Thompson, George. *Bat Masterson: The Dodge City Years.* Topeka: Kansas State College, 1943

Tilghman, Zoe. *Marshal of the Last Frontier.* Glendale, Calif.: Arthur H. Clark Co., 1949

Vestal, Stanley. *Dodge City: Queen of Cowtowns.* New York: Harper and Brothers, 1952

INDEX

187

About the Author

DALE WHITE was born in Gary, Indiana, and grew up in Indiana, Minnesota and Florida. She holds a B.S. in Library Science from the University of Minnesota and a B.A. from Rollins College in Florida. She worked as a fine arts librarian at Rollins, doing newspaper free-lance reporting on the side. She married the son of a Montana pioneering family and moved to Montana where she and her family are still living. She writes fiction as well as non-fiction for young people, and has to her credit several Junior Literary Guild selections as well as the Silver Spur Award presented by the Western Writers of America for the "Best Western Juvenile" published in 1958.